Nonfiction Reading Comprehension

3–4

Written by
Pamela Jennett

Editors: Carla Hamaguchi and Collene Dobelmann
Illustrator: Darcy Tom
Designer/Production: Moonhee Pak/Andrea Ables
Cover Designer: Barbara Peterson
Art Director: Tom Cochrane
Project Director: Carolea Williams

Table of Contents

Introduction

Each book in the *Power Practice*™ series contains dozens of ready-to-use activity pages to provide students with skill practice. Use the fun activities to supplement and enhance what you are already teaching in your classroom. Give an activity page to students as independent class work, or send the pages home as homework to reinforce skills taught in class. An answer key is provided for quick reference.

Nonfiction reading is different than reading fiction or reading for pleasure. Students read nonfiction books and articles to find information, learn about new ideas and subjects, or find out more about a topic that interests them. The text features of nonfiction reading materials are different from the features of fiction, and the associated comprehension skills are also different. *Nonfiction Reading Comprehension 3-4* gives students practice with topics that are appropriate for their grade level. Students use the features particular to nonfiction as they read and comprehend the selections. The controlled vocabulary and reading level of the passages allows them to focus on the accompanying skills pages.

Nonfiction Reading Comprehension 3–4 is a collection of units featuring a nonfiction passage with accompanying vocabulary, comprehension, reading strategy, and word study exercises. These reproducibles give students practice in a focus skill that is based on a nonfiction selection. Each mini-unit provides practice of skills in a format they may encounter in a standardized-testing situation.

Use these ready-to-go activities to "recharge" skill review and give students the power to succeed!

Your Skeleton

Most of your body is squishy and soft. Not your bones! Bones are very hard. Bones give your body shape. They help keep you standing up tall. Bones also protect the soft organs on the inside. All of your bones together make up your skeleton.

Bones come in many shapes and sizes. The biggest bone in your body is in your leg. It is your thighbone. The thighbone is also called the femur. The smallest bone in your body is in your ear. It is a tiny little bone called the stirrup. It transfers vibrations from your eardrum to the inner ear.

The bones of your head make up your skull. The skull surrounds the most important organ in your body, the brain. The skull protects the brain from knocks and bumps. The cranium is the top part of the skull. Eight bones fit tightly together to form the cranium. It acts like a helmet around your brain.

Down the center of your back is your backbone. You can feel bumps just under the skin. These bumps are the bones in your backbone. They are called vertebrae. The vertebrae are stacked on top of each other. Between each one is a pad of cartilage that cushions your spine as you jump and move. Your backbone is special. It lets you bend forward, backward, and side to side. It can swivel in both directions.

Joints connect bones to each other. Joints allow you to move those rigid bones. Your elbows and knees are joints. Your ankles and wrists are joints. Some joints only allow you to move your body parts in one direction. Other joints let you move body parts in many directions.

Bones are living and growing parts of the body. Like the rest of your body, bones need exercise and healthy food. Take good care of your bones so they can take care of you.

Nonfiction Reading Comprehension • 3-4 © 2005 Creative Teaching Press

Name _____ Date _____

Define Vocabulary

These words are found in the passage "Your Skeleton." Match each word from the word box to its definition.

skeleton	organs	femur	cranium	vertebrae
joints	rigid	direction	cartilage	cushions

1. _____ Cartilage does this. It lessons the force between your bones.

2. _____ This word describes your bones. It means that they are stiff.

3. _____ This is the name for the top part of your skull. It acts like a helmet for your brain.

4. _____ This word describes the way in which joints allow your bones to move. Some can only move one way. Others can move many ways.

5. _____ These connect bones to each other. They allow us to move.

6. _____ This is what we call all of the bones in your body.

7. _____ These are soft things inside your body. They do special jobs. Your bones protect some of them.

8. _____ This is the largest bone in your body.

9. _____ These bones make up your backbone. They help you stand up tall.

10. _____ A pad of this material is found between your vertebrae. It helps cushion your bones.

Nonfiction Reading Comprehension • 3–4 © 2005 Creative Teaching Press

Recall Information

Recall what you learned in "Your Skeleton." Circle the letter next to the answer that best completes the sentence.

1 Bones are not
a. rigid.
b. squishy.
c. living.
d. growing.

2 Bones are connected together by
a. skulls.
b. joints.
c. bumps.
d. healthy food.

3 The skull protects the most important organ, your
a. brain.
b. heart.
c. liver.
d. bones.

4 You should take care of your bones so they
a. disappear.
b. stay soft and ripe.
c. do not leak water.
d. stay healthy and strong.

5 The stirrup is
a. the smallest bone in your body.
b. the largest bone in your body.
c. the softest bone in your body.
d. something that helps you move.

6 Elbows, knees, ankles, and wrists are examples of
a. people.
b. organs.
c. joints.
d. directions.

7 Joints help us
a. sweat.
b. think.
c. sleep.
d. move.

8 Bones need
a. exercise.
b. healthy food.
c. good care.
d. all of these.

Name _____ Date _____

Identify Main Idea and Details

The **main idea** states the most important idea of a paragraph or passage. **Supporting details** are small pieces of information that tell more about the main idea.

Write the sentence choice that forms the main idea for each paragraph.

 _____.
The marrow is the center part of the bone and produces red blood cells. Spongy bone gives the bone strength without weight. Compact bone is hard and smooth. Each bone has a covering to which the muscles attach.
- **a.** Almost every bone is made of the same material.
- **b.** Parts of bones have silly names.
- **c.** Bones are made up of living cells.

 _____
Your ribs act like a cage around your chest. They protect your heart, lungs, and liver. Your skull is like a helmet. It protects your brain from injury.
- **a.** Some bones give our body support.
- **b.** The place where two bones meet is called a joint.
- **c.** Some bones shield the organs in the body.

 _____
The largest bone is the femur. It is the bone in your upper leg and supports your weight as you move. The smallest bone is the stirrup in your inner ear. It is less than an inch long.
- **a.** The smallest bones are found in the inner ear.
- **b.** Bones allow you to move.
- **c.** Bones come in different sizes.

 _____
Wear the proper equipment, like a helmet, kneepads, or wrist guards, while playing sports. Eat a healthy diet rich in calcium. Exercise so your bones stay strong.
- **a.** Bones can be injured during sports.
- **b.** Take care of your bones and they will take care of you.
- **c.** Bones can be broken and take a long time to heal.

Nonfiction Reading Comprehension • 3–4 © 2005 Creative Teaching Press

Name _____   Date _____

Identify Nouns, Verbs, and Adjectives

Nouns are words that name a person, place, thing, or idea. • children • beach • volleyball • freedom	**Verbs** are words that describe action or states of being. • are • is running • swam • flies	**Adjectives** are words that describe nouns. They usually come before the noun. • <u>silly</u> child • <u>twenty</u> bones Adjectives follow the noun when a linking verb is used. • The teacher is <u>kind</u>. • Children are <u>happy</u>.

Circle the correct letter to tell if the underlined word is a noun, a verb, or an adjective.

1 The femur is a very <u>large</u> bone.
  a. noun
  b. verb
  c. adjective

2 Your <u>spine</u> holds your body upright.
  a. noun
  b. verb
  c. adjective

3 Your spine <u>twists</u> this way and that.
  a. noun
  b. verb
  c. adjective

4 Bones in your feet <u>help</u> you stand and walk.
  a. noun
  b. verb
  c. adjective

5 The sternum is a <u>strong</u> bone in the center of your chest.
  a. noun
  b. verb
  c. adjective

6 Your jawbone <u>opens</u> and closes to talk and chew food.
  a. noun
  b. verb
  c. adjective

7 The pelvis is a bowl-shaped <u>structure</u> that supports your backbone.
  a. noun
  b. verb
  c. adjective

8 The inner ear is made up of <u>three</u> bones.
  a. noun
  b. verb
  c. adjective

9 <u>Adults</u> have 206 bones.
  a. noun
  b. verb
  c. adjective

10 Your <u>skeleton</u> is both very strong and very light.
  a. noun
  b. verb
  c. adjective

Sounds All Around

Sound is all around us. Some sounds are loud like a honking horn. Some sounds are soft like the buzz of a bee. Think of sounds you hear every day. What is sound?

Sound is caused by a back-and-forth movement called vibration. Hum a note and feel the tiny vibrations. As the vocal cords move back and forth, they make the air move back and forth. These vibrations travel through the air until they reach someone else's eardrum. The eardrum begins to move as the air vibrations hit it. The person hears a sound.

Sounds can be high or low. This is called pitch. A high-pitched sound moves really fast. A low-pitched sound moves very slowly. Sounds can also be loud or soft. This is called intensity. A big vibration makes a loud sound. A small vibration makes a soft sound.

Sound moves in waves. Think about what happens when a pebble is dropped into a pool of water. Waves move out from the center. Sound travels in the same way. Sound moves out from a vibrating object in all directions. The farther the sound travels, the weaker the vibrations get.

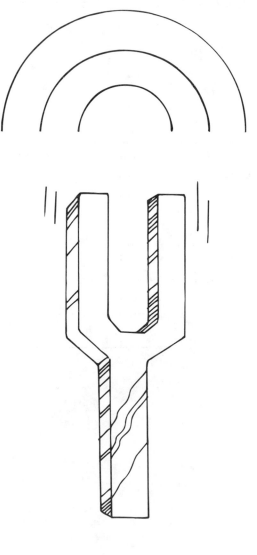

Most sounds we hear move through the air. The air is a gas. Sounds can move through liquids and solids, too. In fact, sound waves move better through liquids than gases. They travel even better through solids than liquids. Tap a finger lightly on the surface of a table. Notice how loud the sound is. Now set your ear against the surface and tap the same way as before. The sound seems louder because the vibrations are moving through the solid table, instead of the air.

Nonfiction Reading Comprehension • 3–4 © 2005 Creative Teaching Press

Solve a Vocabulary Puzzle

Use the vocabulary words from the passage "Sounds All Around" to complete the crossword puzzle.

vibration	pitch	intensity	gas
liquid	solid	wave	direction

Across

2. a state of matter that can expand to fill a container
4. the highness or lowness of a sound
6. a line or course along which something moves or travels
7. a motion that moves up and down or back and forth, passing energy from one point to another
8. the loudness or softness of a sound

Down

1. rapid movement back and forth
3. a state of matter that has a definite size and shape
5. a state of matter that flows easily and is hard to compress

Name _____ Date _____

Determine Cause and Effect

A **cause** is why something happens. An **effect** is what happens.

Gracie covered her ears when the cannon went off.

| Cause: The cannon went off. | → | Effect: Gracie covered her ears. |

Sometimes words signal a cause and effect. *Because*, *since*, and *when* are clue words that signal a cause and effect. Other times there are no clue words. You must think about the cause and effect on your own.

For each sentence write the cause in the first box and the effect it had in the second box.

1 Because the bell was so loud, everyone jumped in their seats.

| Cause | → | Effect |

2 The spinning metal blades caused a whirring sound.

| Cause | → | Effect |

3 Vibrations in the air reach the eardrum and we hear a sound.

| Cause | → | Effect |

4 The clanging of the pipes was louder because I was underwater.

| Cause | → | Effect |

5 Since the sound waves move fast, we hear a high-pitched sound.

| Cause | → | Effect |

6 The farther sound travels, the weaker it gets.

| Cause | → | Effect |

Nonfiction Reading Comprehension • 3–4 © 2005 Creative Teaching Press

Name _____ Date _____

Choose Key Words

Imagine you want to find out how the ear is damaged by loud sounds. If you went to the library, what would you look for? You could look under *human body, ear, hearing damage,* or *loud sounds.* Which do you think would most likely have the information you wanted? Thinking about key words will help you find what you need.

Circle the letter of the key word that will best help you find information about each topic.

1 You want to learn how feathers help a bird to fly.
    a. space flight
    b. ostrich feathers
    c. bird flight

2 You want to learn about Thomas Edison's inventions that helped the deaf.
    a. deafness
    b. Edison's inventions
    c. Edison's early years

3 You want to know how to make a model of a telephone.
    a. telephone history
    b. telephone inventor
    c. telephone model

4 You want to know how long the coastline of Florida is.
    a. Florida geography
    b. Florida history
    c. Florida sports

5 You want to find out when baseball was invented.
    a. baseball humor
    b. baseball history
    c. baseball rules

6 You want to know if hamsters can eat walnuts.
    a. hamster habitat
    b. walnuts
    c. hamster care

7 You want to know what the state bird of Ohio is.
    a. Ohio geography
    b. Ohio government
    c. Ohio symbols

8 You want to know how far a kangaroo can hop.
    a. Australia
    b. kangaroo habitat
    c. kangaroo facts

Compare with Adjectives

To compare two things, add *-er* to the word. To compare three or more things, add *-est* to the word. Add the correct ending to each word to complete the chart.

		Comparing Two Things	Comparing Three or More Things
1	soft		
2	loud		
3	weak		
4	fast		
5	slow		

Some words do not show comparison by adding *-er* or *-est*. The word changes to compare. Circle the correct word in each column.

		Compare Two Things	Compare Three or More Things
6	good	gooder or better	best or goodest
7	bad	worse or badder	worst or baddest

Complete each sentence by writing the correct form of the adjective in parentheses.

8 A high-pitched sound moves _____ than a low-pitched sound. (fast)

9 Between a solid, liquid, and gas, sound moves _____ through a solid. (good)

10 A whisper is a _____ sound than a scream. (weak)

11 Of all the sounds I hear, a whisper is the _____. (soft)

12 What is the _____ sound you have heard today? (loud)

Nonfiction Reading Comprehension • 3–4 © 2005 Creative Teaching Press

Ants

Ants are insects. Like other insects, they have three body parts: a head, a thorax, and an abdomen. Their three pairs of legs are jointed. They have antennae to help them sense things.

Ants belong to a group of insects that includes bees and wasps. This group of insects has bent antennae and mouths made to chew things. They have indented abdomens. This makes them look like they have a narrow waist.

Ants are social animals. They live in colonies. Each ant colony has a queen and her children. The females are the workers. The worker ants have special jobs. Many look for food. Others build the nest. Some protect the nest from danger. Only a very few of the children are male. Their only job is to mate with the queen. The queen's job is to produce new baby ants.

Ants communicate with each other. They use chemical scents from their bodies to pass on messages. They can alert others to danger. They can guide each other to food. This is why we see long lines of ants leading away from a nest. Ants mark the boundaries of their colony. They even use scent to tell when a colony member has died. When a dead ant is discovered, it is carried outside.

Ants are important to the habitats where they live. Many dig under the ground. This breaks up the soil and brings air and water to the roots of plants. Some ants move seeds around. This helps plants grow in new places. Some ants feed on other insect pests. Ants are also a source of food for other animals.

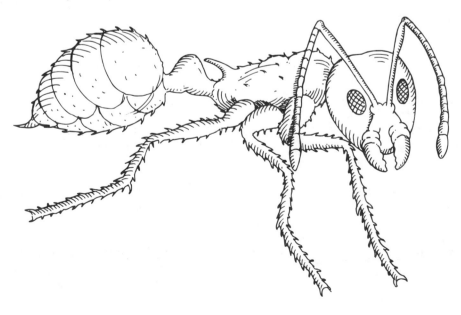

Name _____ Date _____

Match Vocabulary

Draw a line to match each word from the passage "Ants" with its meaning.

1 thorax

2 abdomen

3 indented

4 jointed

5 antennae

6 communicate

7 chemical

8 boundaries

a. the section of an insect's body furthest from the head

b. a substance produced by combining atoms or molecules

c. when two or more sections come together

d. the middle section of an insect's body

e. to trade information

f. lines or limits where something ends

g. having a middle part thinner than the surrounding parts

h. a pair of thin, movable sensory organs on an insect's head

Use the vocabulary words from above to complete the sentences.

9 The legs connect to the _____, or center section, of the body.

10 The _____ is the part of an ant's body farthest from its head.

11 Ants use their antennae to sense _____ smells.

12 Ants _____ to tell about food or danger.

13 Ants have three pairs of _____ legs.

14 The thorax is _____, making the ant look like it has a tiny waist.

15 Ants form chemical _____ around their colonies to keep other ants away.

16 By using their _____, ants can communicate with each other.

Nonfiction Reading Comprehension • 3–4 © 2005 Creative Teaching Press

Summarize Ideas

To **summarize** means to briefly tell the most important parts of a paragraph or passage. Circle the statement that best summarizes each paragraph.

Write the sentence choice that forms the main idea for each paragraph.

1 Honey is produced by certain kinds of bees from the nectar of flowers. Many insects eat nectar, but honeybees are the only ones that use the nectar to make honey. They make honey and store it in their hive. In the winter, they cannot find nectar. The bees eat the honey to stay active and keep warm during the cold weather.

Summary: Bees use flower nectar to make honey to use as food.
Bees produce different kinds of honey for the winter.

2 The praying mantis is an interesting insect that is a carnivore. It eats other insects. This makes the mantis especially useful in gardens. The mantis preys on insects that are pests to gardeners and farmers. It eats pests like aphids, moths, flies, and caterpillars. Mantises also eat each other!

Summary: Carnivores are useful insects to gardeners and farmers.
The praying mantis eats insects that are pests to gardeners and farmers.

3 When you think of termites, do you think of nasty bugs chewing through the walls of your home? Termites are pests because they eat and digest wood. This can mean trouble for a building. However, termites can be helpful as well. They chew up and break down plant matter. In this way, termites recycle the nutrients in wood. Then the nutrients can be used by other living plants.

Summary: Termites are both troublesome and helpful because they eat wood.
Termites eat living plants and other things made of wood.

Read a Diagram

Reading a diagram helps us understand what we read. A **diagram** is a picture with labels. The labels explain each part of a whole picture.

Match each label on the diagram to its description.

abdomen ——————
wings ——————
pollen basket ——————

stinger ——————

head ——————
antennae ——————
compound eye ——————

mandibles ——————
proboscis ——————

1 _____ This segmented tail area contains the heart, wax glands, and most of the digestive system.

2 _____ This is a pair of appendages on the head of a bee used to sense its surroundings.

3 _____ This is a large eye made up of many hexagon-shaped lenses.

4 _____ Attached to the thorax, the two pairs of these allow bees to fly.

5 _____ This part of the insect contains the brain, eyes, proboscis, and mandibles.

6 _____ Located on the hind legs, this is used to carry pollen back to the hive.

7 _____ These two jaws are located on the lower side of the head.

8 _____ This straw-like tongue attaches to the head.

9 _____ This sharp shaft is located at the end of the abdomen and used for defense.

Nonfiction Reading Comprehension • 3–4 © 2005 Creative Teaching Press

Name _____ Date _____

Know Word Roots

A **root** is the basic part of a word. Some roots are based on Greek or Latin words. By knowing what a root means, we can often figure out the meaning of a word that contains it. These are common roots found in science words:

Greek roots: *geo:* earth   *micro:* small   *chron:* time
Latin roots: *port:* to carry   *scrib:* to write   *pend:* to hang

For each word underline the root from the list above found within the word. Then circle the most likely definition based on the meaning of the root.

1 geology   study of time   study of the earth, rocks

2 pendulum   an object that hangs   an object that is small

3 chronicle   a recording of songs   a record of events over time

4 geographer   a person who studies   a person who writes
                       the earth

5 synchronize   to make something happen   to watch something hang
                       at the same time

6 microbe   a mineral of the earth   a very small living thing

7 inscribe   to write words into   to carry something
                       something

8 appendage   a part of the body that hangs   a part of the earth that
                       down from another part   sticks out into water

9 export   to write out   to carry out

10 portable   able to keep time   able to be carried

Erosion

Over time, rocks on the surface of the earth change. Erosion is one way rocks can be changed. Erosion happens when rock parts are moved away. Wind, water, and glaciers all cause erosion.

Water can erode rock quickly. Waves in a big lake or ocean splash against rocks. The waves rub off or break away pieces of rock. Waves also move rocks and sand from the shore. Water runs through rivers and streams. The moving water erodes away rocks and soil. The river cuts deeper to make a canyon. The Grand Canyon is an amazing example of how a river can cut through rock.

Wind erodes rock just like water does. The wind picks up small particles of dirt or sand. It whips the particles against other rocks. This wears away the rock almost like sandpaper wears away wood. The force of the wind wears away soft rock faster than hard rock. This can make an interesting rock formation that looks like a statue.

Glaciers erode rock very slowly. A glacier is a large sheet of moving ice or snow. All of that ice is massive. As a glacier slides downhill, it carries away rock and sand. The glacier scrapes up the earth and pushes it along. Glaciers can sculpt valleys and lakes. The Great Lakes were carved out by glaciers long ago.

Look at the land around you. Can you find rocks that were changed by erosion?

Nonfiction Reading Comprehension • 3–4 © 2005 Creative Teaching Press

Name _____ Date _____

Define Vocabulary

These words are found in the passage "Erosion." Match each word from the word box to its definition.

surface	erode	glacier	canyon	formation
particle	statue	massive	scrape	sculpt

1 _____ This verb means to "carve out."

2 _____ This adjective describes something that is large, solid, and heavy.

3 _____ This verb means "to remove material by rubbing or dragging two things against each other."

4 _____ This action word means "to wear away."

5 _____ This noun is a shape or an arrangement.

6 _____ This noun is a very small piece or amount.

7 _____ This noun is a large mass of ice that moves slowly down a mountain or through a valley.

8 _____ This noun is a deep valley with steep sides that was formed by running water.

9 _____ This noun is an image that has been carved out of a solid material like stone.

10 _____ This noun is the outer layer.

Name _____ Date _____

Determine Sequence

Sequence is the order in which things happen. Words such as *then* and *after* are often clues to the sequence. By arranging events in sequence, you can see how one thing leads to another.

Read each set of sentences. Number the sentences 1 to 5 to put each set in the correct sequence.

A. _____ Then snow builds up to form a glacier.

_____ The rubbing of the moving glacier at last carves a valley.

_____ After many winters, the glacier is very large and heavy.

_____ At first the snow falls for many days.

_____ Over time, gravity pulls the glacier down the mountain.

B. _____ After a long time, a deep canyon is formed.

_____ The streams become rivers and carry away bits of dirt and sand.

_____ As the rain runs over the ground, it forms small streams.

_____ Then rushing water of the rivers cuts into the rock and sand.

_____ At first the rain begins to fall.

C. _____ Then the sand and sediment are hurled against the rock.

_____ The swirling winds pick up bits of sand and sediment.

_____ At first the wind begins to blow.

_____ After many years, the rock is worn away to form new shapes.

_____ The moving bits rub like sandpaper against the rock.

Nonfiction Reading Comprehension • 3–4 © 2005 Creative Teaching Press

Name _____ Date _____

Read a Map Diagram

A map diagram can help you understand new vocabulary about the features of the earth. Use the diagram to label the missing terms. Then answer the questions.

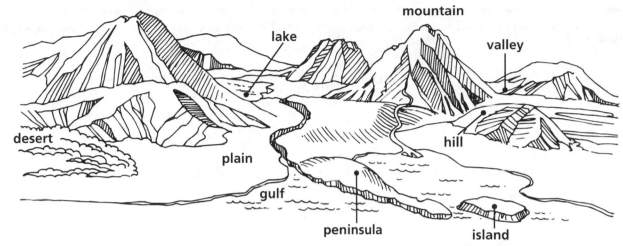

1 _____ : a large dry area of land

2 _____ : a large body of ocean water that is partly surrounded by land

3 _____ : a landform with water all around it

4 _____ : land that rises above the land around it

5 _____ : the highest kind of land

6 _____ : a body of water with land on all sides

7 _____ : a flat area of land

8 _____ : low land between hills or mountains

9 What bodies of water are shown in the diagram?

_____

10 What kinds of land are shown in the diagram?

_____

11 How is an island different from a peninsula?

_____

12 How is a hill different from a mountain?

_____

Name _____ Date _____

Choose Synonyms

Synonyms are words that have the same or almost the same meaning.

Circle all of the words in each row that have the same meaning as the first word.

1. **massive**	large	huge	accident	bulky
2. **scrape**	scuff	remove	ooze	scratch
3. **sculpt**	paste	carve	search	whittle
4. **quick**	hasty	rapid	swift	begin
5. **wind**	breeze	joke	gale	branch
6. **slow**	unhurried	idle	active	smack
7. **rock**	stone	boulder	pebble	roll
8. **look**	hide	view	imagine	watch
9. **earth**	star	planet	world	moon
10. **stream**	brook	creek	lake	ribbon

Nonfiction Reading Comprehension • 3–4 © 2005 Creative Teaching Press

Using Maps

A map is a picture that shows where places are found. A map can show a large area of land. A map can show where things are located in a building. Each map is made to show certain details.

A physical map shows land and water. This kind of map might show one of the continents. It might only show the land and water of a small section of land. A geographical map shows where you can find lakes and rivers. It shows the location of mountains and deserts. The map gives the names of some of the bigger features. Colors on the map show where land is high and low. Blue is used to show the bodies of water.

A political map shows where one place ends and another begins. This map shows the borders of continents, nations, states, and other regions. Different colors show each place. A political map might show bodies of water that form a border, but it does not show other landforms.

Some maps have a special purpose. A street map shows how to get around a city or neighborhood. A product map shows where crops are grown and certain goods are made. A historical map shows where important events from the past happened. A bird's-eye map shows our location. It might show where we are in a building. It might show how to take a train from one place to another.

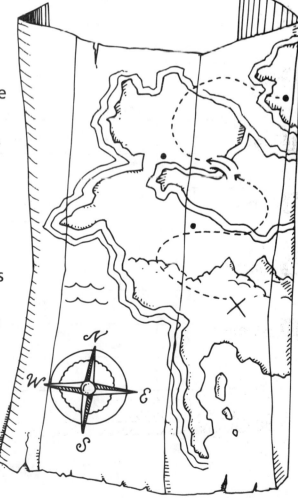

Maps have certain features that give us information. Map symbols are small pictures that stand for the real thing. A map key tells what each symbol stands for. A map scale helps us find the distance from one place to another. A compass rose shows the cardinal directions: north, south, east, and west. A map grid divides a map into squares so we can find locations on the map.

Nonfiction Reading Comprehension • 3–4 © 2005 Creative Teaching Press

Solve a Vocabulary Puzzle

Match each word in the word box to a clue to complete the crossword puzzle.

| detail | physical | continent | geography |
| feature | nation | purpose | symbol |

Across
1. the reason or point of doing something
3. the land features of a region or place
4. something that stands for or represents something else
5. a part or quality of something that you notice
6. a small part of a whole
7. another name for a country

Down
1. of or relating to matter that is not living
2. one of the main land masses of Earth

Nonfiction Reading Comprehension • 3–4 © 2005 Creative Teaching Press

Draw Conclusions

When you draw conclusions you combine what you already know with what you learn. Use the information from the passage "Using Maps" and your own knowledge to choose the best answer for each question.

1 If you wanted to know how to drive from your house to the nearest museum, which map would be most useful?
    a. physical map
    b. political map
    c. street map
    d. historical map

2 If you wanted to know where the major battles of the Civil War happened, which map would be most useful?
    a. physical map
    b. political map
    c. street map
    d. historical map

3 Where would you most likely find the height of the tallest mountain in your state?
    a. physical map
    b. geography map
    c. street map
    d. historical map

4 Where would you discover what countries border Switzerland?
    a. physical map
    b. political map
    c. street map
    d. historical map

5 Where would you find out which states grow wheat?
    a. product map
    b. bird's-eye map
    c. street map
    d. historical map

6 Where would you look to find out where the restrooms are in a building?
    a. product map
    b. bird's-eye map
    c. street map
    d. historical map

7 Which of these map features would help you find the distance from your town to the nearest lake?
    a. map key
    b. compass rose
    c. map grid
    d. map scale

Name _____ Date _____

Use Map Features

Most maps include a legend, compass rose, and scale. The **map legend** tells the meaning of the symbols. The **compass rose** gives the directions. The **map scale** tells how far it is from one place to another.

Use these features on the map below to answer the questions.

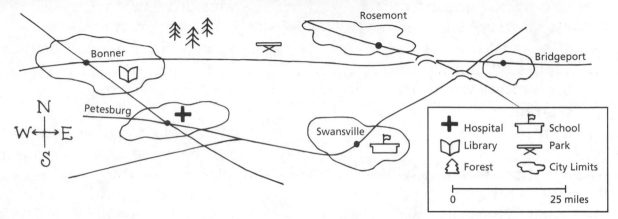

1 From Petesburg to Swansville you travel in which direction?
   a. north
   b. south
   c. east
   d. west

2 Which symbol represents the hospital on the map?
   a. cross
   b. book
   c. building with flag
   d. tree

3 What is the approximate distance from Petesburg to Bonner?
   a. 15 miles
   b. 50 miles
   c. 35 miles
   d. 25 miles

4 Which locations are farthest apart?
   a. Swansville and Bonner
   b. Bonner and Petesburg
   c. Petesburg and Swansville
   d. Bonner and Bridgeport

5 To drive from Bonner to Bridgeport, which would you not pass?
   a. forest
   b. library
   c. school
   d. park

6 You are in Swansville. Which town is northeast of you?
   a. Petesburg
   b. Bridgeport
   c. Swansville
   d. Bonner

Nonfiction Reading Comprehension • 3–4 © 2005 Creative Teaching Press

Name _____ Date _____

Identify Proper Nouns

A **noun** can be a person, a place, a thing, or an idea. A **proper noun** is the specific name for a person, a place, a thing, or an idea. Proper nouns are capitalized.

All of the words that make up the name of a proper noun are capitalized.	
a river	Columbia River
a mountain	Mount St. Helens
a country	New Zealand
Small words such as *and, in, of,* and *the* are not capitalized.	
an oath	Pledge of Allegiance
a place	Lewis and Clark Trail

Write each proper noun in the word box next to the common noun that describes it. As you write each proper noun, add capital letters where needed.

british columbia	north dakota	cathedral peak
kalahari desert	indian ocean	hawaii
lord of the rings	sheryl crow	george washington
canada	nile	america the beautiful

1 a song _____

2 an island _____

3 a mountain _____

4 an ocean _____

5 a desert _____

6 a president _____

7 a singer _____

8 a province _____

9 a country _____

10 a book _____

11 a state _____

12 a river _____

The Inner Planets

Our solar system is all the planets, moons, and other heavenly bodies that circle around our sun. There are nine planets in our solar system. The four closest to the sun are called the inner planets. The inner planets are Mercury, Venus, Earth, and Mars.

Mercury is the closest planet to the sun. It orbits, or circles around, the sun quickly. Mercury makes one circle around the sun in 88 days. The surface gets very hot and very cold. We do not think Mercury has any moons.

Venus is the second planet from the sun. We can see Venus early in the morning or early at night. Thick clouds cover Venus. The clouds reflect sunlight. This makes it appear bright in our sky. Venus is about the same size as Earth. It is still closer to the sun. In about 225 days, Venus travels around the sun. Venus does not seem to have any moons.

Our planet, Earth, is third from the sun. Most of its surface is covered with water. It looks blue from outer space. Clouds swirl over the surface. White ice covers the poles. It takes a little more than 365 days for Earth to circle the sun. Earth has one moon.

The last inner planet is Mars. Mars is called the "red planet" because of its orange-red color. The color comes from the rusty iron in the rocks on its surface. Mars circles the sun in about 686 days. It is about half the size of Earth. Like Earth, Mars has mountains, valleys, polar ice caps, and dry river beds. Mars is circled by two small moons.

We know a lot about the inner planets. There is still a lot more we can learn.

Nonfiction Reading Comprehension • 3–4 © 2005 Creative Teaching Press

Name _____ Date _____

Match Vocabulary

Draw a line to match each word from the passage "The Inner Planets" with its meaning.

1) solar   **a.** to send back the sun's rays off a surface

2) system   **b.** of or near the North or South Pole.

3) orbit   **c.** relating to the sun

4) reflect   **d.** to move with a rotating motion

5) seem   **e.** the path of a planet as it travels around the sun

6) swirl   **f.** covered with a reddish-brown coating

7) rusty   **g.** to appear a certain way

8) polar   **h.** a set of parts that work together as one unit

Use four words from above to complete the sentences.

9) The planets in our solar system _____ around the sun.

10) The child's bicycle seemed _____ and old.

11) The polar ice caps _____ sunlight back into space.

12) We watched the mist _____ over the grass in the park.

Nonfiction Reading Comprehension • 3–4 © 2005 Creative Teaching Press

Name _____ Date _____

Reread and Recall Facts

You can reread a passage to help you recall answers about what you have read. Use the words in the word box to complete the paragraph. Reread "The Inner Planets" to help you recall any answers you have missed.

valleys	nine	red	inner planets	clouds
heavenly	sunlight	ice	polar	rusty
iron	closest	dry	water	caps

Our solar system is made up of _____ planets. The planets,

1

moons, asteroids, and other _____ bodies orbit the sun. Mercury,

2

Venus, Earth, and Mars are known as the _____ _____.

3

Mercury is _____ to the sun, so it gets really hot and really cold.

4

Venus is covered by thick _____ that reflect _____.

5   6

Earth is our planet. From space it appears blue because it is covered with

_____. The poles appear white because they are covered with

7

_____. Mars is known as the _____ planet. This is because

8   9

its surface appears _____ in color because of the _____

10   11

in its rocks. Mars is like Earth because it also has mountains, _____,

12

_____ river beds, and _____ ice _____.

13   14   15

Nonfiction Reading Comprehension • 3–4 © 2005 Creative Teaching Press

Name _____ Date _____

Read a Table

A **table** is a way to organize and show information. The information is shown in rows and columns. This table shows a list of the planets in our solar system. The planets are listed in their order from the sun.

Facts about Our Solar System

Name of Planet	Number of Moons	Length of Year (in Earth days)	Rings Around Planet	Surface Temperature (in degrees celsius)
Mercury	0	88	no	167°
Venus	0	225	no	464°
Earth	1	365	no	15°
Mars	2	687	no	-65°
Jupiter	39	4,331	yes	-110°
Saturn	30	10,747	yes	-140°
Uranus	21	30,589	yes	-195°
Neptune	8	59,800	yes	-200°
Pluto	1	90,588	no	-225°

Use the table to answer the questions.

1. Which planets do not have rings?_____

2. Which planet has 30 moons? _____

3. Which planet takes longer to orbit the sun, Jupiter or Mars? _____

4. Which has fewer moons, Earth or Pluto? _____

5. Which is the coldest planet? Why? _____

6. Look at the surface temperatures of the planets. What can you infer happens as the planets get farther from the sun? _____

Use Subject and Verb Agreement

The verb must agree with the subject in number. If the noun stands for one person, place, or thing, the verb most likely will end with –s or –es. If the subject stands for more than one, the verb most likely will NOT end with –s or –es. Watch for verbs that end in –y. The y needs to change to i before adding –es.

Circle the correct form of the verb that completes the sentence.

1. Heavenly bodies (circle circles) the sun.

2. Clouds (cover covers) the surface of Venus.

3. The surface (heat heats) up rapidly during the day.

4. The planet Venus (measure measures) about the same size as Earth.

5. My class (studys studies) facts about the planets.

6. Two moons (orbit orbits) around Mars.

7. Dry river beds (appear appears) on the surface of Mars.

8. Ocean water (look looks) blue from outer space.

9. Scientists (learn learns) more about the planets every year.

10. My sister (spys spies) Venus through her telescope at night.

Nonfiction Reading Comprehension • 3–4 © 2005 Creative Teaching Press

The Mayflower Compact

In 1620, a small, crowded ship left England. It was sailing for the New World. On board were a group of men and women called Pilgrims. They had not had an easy life. They wanted to worship in a simpler way. Other people would not let them. They had been forced to leave their homes. Now they hoped that if they went to the New World, they could worship the way they wanted. As the *Mayflower* got ready to leave, more people joined the voyage. They did not share the Pilgrims' religion. They were called "strangers." The strangers also wanted to start a new life in a new place.

As the ship crossed the ocean, the Pilgrims saw problems. Some of the people did not listen to others. The strangers said they would not follow any rules. They would not listen to the Pilgrim leaders. Most of the people knew they needed an agreement. It would apply to all the people. It would tell how they would rule themselves. It would tell what laws should be made.

Before the *Mayflower* landed, the Pilgrims and strangers met around a table in the captain's room. There, they signed their names to a piece of paper. This piece of paper was an agreement called the Mayflower Compact. Anyone who signed it agreed to work together. They would create laws for the colony that were fair and equal. Every man signed the Mayflower Compact before he left the ship. The Mayflower Compact shows that the colonists were concerned about the whole group. They were willing to work together. They would make laws that were fair for all.

Nonfiction Reading Comprehension • 3–4 © 2005 Creative Teaching Press

Name _____ Date _____

Solve a Vocabulary Puzzle

Use the vocabulary words from the passage "The Mayflower Compact" to complete the crossword puzzle.

crowded	forced	worship	religion	crossed
agreement	rule	colonists	law	

Across

2. a rule that regulates the behavior of a group of people
4. made to do something
6. filled with many people or things
8. a statement that controls behavior or action
9. people who settle in a distant land

Down

1. went to the other side of something
3. an arrangement or understanding between people or groups
5. a belief in and the worship of God or gods
7. to take part in a religious service

Nonfiction Reading Comprehension • 3–4 © 2005 Creative Teaching Press

Infer Sequence

Sometimes a nonfiction passage will give events in the same order they happen. Other times you must use what you have learned and what you know to find the sequence. The statements below are from the Mayflower Compact. Number the statements from 1 to 10 to place them in the correct order. If necessary, reread "The Mayflower Compact" to check your answers.

_____ The Pilgrims decided an agreement was needed.

_____ The Pilgrims decided to leave for the New World.

_____ Strangers joined the Pilgrims for the voyage.

_____ The Pilgrims were forced from their homes.

_____ Problems arose during the ocean crossing.

_____ The *Mayflower* landed in the New World.

_____ The Pilgrims and strangers met in the captain's quarters.

_____ The Pilgrims and strangers went ashore at Plymouth Rock.

_____ The *Mayflower* left England.

_____ Every man signed the Mayflower Compact.

Now rewrite the sentences in the correct order as a paragraph. Add sequence words such as *after that* and *in the end* to guide readers from one event to the next.

_____

_____

_____

_____

_____

_____

Name _____ Date _____

Read a Chart

Many textbooks, reference books, and other nonfiction sources contain tables. A **table** is a way to organize and show information. Charts may include words and numbers in the form of lists. Read this chart of information about early New World settlements.

Roanoke, Virginia	Plymouth, Massachusetts	Jamestown, Virginia
• founded by Sir Walter Raleigh	• founded by Pilgrims	• founded by Virginia Company
• purpose: trading	• purpose: religious freedom	• purpose: trading
• started in 1585	• started in 1620	• started in 1607
• 108 people	• 102 people	• 108 people
• at north end of an island	• on the coast	

Write **true** or **false** for each statement. Use information from the chart to help you label each statement.

1 _____ Plymouth and Roanoke were both started for religious reasons.

2 _____ Plymouth was the earliest of the three settlements.

3 _____ Roanoke and Jamestown were founded for the same purpose.

4 _____ Jamestown was located on an island in a river.

5 _____ Jamestown and Roanoke both started with 108 people.

6 _____ Jamestown was founded 22 years after Roanoke.

Nonfiction Reading Comprehension • 3–4 © 2005 Creative Teaching Press

Name _____ Date _____

Identify Words as Nouns or Verbs

Sometimes the same word can be either a noun or a verb. You must read the sentence to see how the word is used. Read each sentence. Write **noun** or **verb** to tell how the underlined word is used.

1 The <u>force</u> of the wind blew the ship off course. _____

2 The Pilgrims were <u>forced</u> to leave their homes. _____

3 Their <u>hope</u> was to find religious freedom in a new place. _____

4 A list of <u>rules</u> was needed to keep the peace. _____

5 A <u>crowd</u> gathered on the deck as land was sighted. _____

6 As the ship <u>crossed</u> the ocean, it battled many storms. _____

7 Immigrants today <u>hope</u> they will find a good life here. _____

8 The Pilgrims built a <u>cross</u> in honor of their safe passage. _____

9 The people <u>crowded</u> together to hear the captain speak. _____

10 No king or queen would <u>rule</u> them in the New World. _____

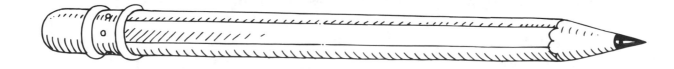

Nonfiction Reading Comprehension • 3–4 © 2005 Creative Teaching Press

Making Mountains

What is a mountain? A mountain is an area of land that rises to a great height. Mountains are all around us. They are on every continent. They are even under the oceans.

Mountains are made in different ways. Some mountains are made by volcanoes. Others are formed when the earth's crust folds over. Some mountains are even made when large rock blocks slide away from each other. Each way forms a different type of mountain.

The earth's crust is divided into plates. The continents and ocean floors are on these plates. The plates slowly move around, pulling apart or pushing together. We cannot see these drifting movements because they happen very slowly. These movements make mountains.

Mountains created by volcanoes can appear quickly. Melted rock erupts from cracks in the earth's crust. The melted rock, or lava, forms layers of rock as it cools. All of these layers make a mountain. Mount St. Helens is a mountain that was created by a volcano.

Folded mountains are made when two plates push together. The pressure folds the rock. The earth's crust bends and buckles, pushing the rock up. The Appalachian Mountains are folded mountains.

Block mountains are made when plates push together but do not bend. Instead, the crust fractures. A rock block slips up, and another slips down. The rock that slips up makes a mountain. The Tetons are block mountains.

Dome mountains are made when melted rock called magma cannot come out of the earth. Instead, it pushes and pushes against the rock on top. The rock bends and forms a dome on the surface. The Black Hills in South Dakota are dome mountains.

Nonfiction Reading Comprehension • 3–4 © 2005 Creative Teaching Press

Name _____ Date _____

Complete Sentences with Vocabulary

These words are found in the passage "Making Mountains." Complete each sentence with a word from the word box.

plates	movements	lava	volcano	layers
pressure	buckle	fracture	magma	dome

1 Melted rock under the surface of the earth is called _____.

2 A break in the rock is called a _____.

3 The crust of the earth is divided into pieces called _____.

4 Mountains are made from _____ of the earth's plates.

5 Once magma flows onto the earth's surface, it is called _____.

6 Sometimes layers of rock bend and _____ to form mountains.

7 Magma pushes up under the rock layers to form a _____ mountain.

8 The _____ from the magma causes the rock to bend.

9 When melted rock erupts from cracks in the earth it forms a

_____.

10 An erupting volcano forms _____ of ash and rock to make a mountain.

Nonfiction Reading Comprehension • 3–4 © 2005 Creative Teaching Press

Find Cause and Effect

Remember that cause and effect tells what happened and gives a reason why an event happened. Use what you learned in "Making Mountains" to choose the best answer.

1 Effect: A mountain is formed.
   Cause: **a.** The plates of the earth's crust move back and forth.
              b. The surface of the earth shrinks and expands.
              c. The water in the ocean covers some of the plates.

2 Cause: Lava erupts from cracks in the earth's crust.
   Effect: **a.** A dome mountain is made.
              b. A plate on the earth's crust appears.
              c. A volcano is formed.

3 Effect: Layers of rock are formed.
   Cause: **a.** Lava mixes with the ocean's water.
              b. Lava flows onto the earth's surface and cools.
              c. Blocks of rock crack and slip against each other.

4 Effect: Folded mountains are formed.
   Cause: **a.** Two blocks push together, slipping and sliding.
              b. Layers of lava flow over each other.
              c. Two plates push together, bending and buckling.

5 Cause: Some rock blocks slip up, while others slip down.
   Effect: **a.** The Tetons were formed.
              b. The Appalachians were formed.
              c. Mount St. Helens was formed.

6 Effect: The rock bends and forms a dome.
   Cause: **a.** The earth's plates pull apart from each other.
              b. Lava erupts and forms many layers.
              c. Trapped magma pushes up against the rock on top.

Nonfiction Reading Comprehension • 3–4 © 2005 Creative Teaching Press

Use Parts of a Book

Different parts of a book are useful when looking for certain kinds of information. The title page and table of contents for a nonfiction book about changes in the earth's surface are shown below. Use this information to answer the questions.

Earth Changes
by Ronald Buckman

Nonfiction Book Publishers, Inc.
New York, NY
2001

Table of Contents

Title Page

Table of Contents

1 What is the title of this book?
   a. Earthquakes
   b. Nonfiction Book Publishers, Inc.
   c. Earth Changes

2 This book was written by whom and in what year?
   a. by Ronald Buckman in 2000
   b. by Ronald Buckman in 2001
   c. by Nonfiction Book Publishers in 2001

3 How many chapters are in this book?
   a. 69
   b. 4
   c. 5

4 Where would you look to find information about how floods change a river's course?
   a. in Chapter 4
   b. in Chapter 3
   c. in Chapter 1

5 On what pages would you most likely find the definition of *magma*?
   a. on pages 23–24
   b. on pages 25–30
   c. on pages 31–35

6 Where would you look to find out more about the 1980 eruption of Mount St. Helens?
   a. under How Volcanoes Are Made
   b. under Famous Volcanoes
   c. under Effects on People

Nonfiction Reading Comprehension • 3–4 © 2005 Creative Teaching Press

Choose Present Tense Verbs

Present tense verbs show what is happening now.

makes   push   bend   buckles   form

If the subject is singular, the verb usually ends in –s or –es.

Tony makes   a layer buckles   the knee bends

If the subject is plural, the verb usual does NOT end in –s or –es.

Tony and Terry make   The layers buckle   The knees bend

Circle the verb in parentheses that correctly completes each sentence.

1. Every year our science club (make makes) a model volcano.

2. Terrence (gather gathers) together the art supplies he will need.

3. Robyn and I (spread spreads) newspapers over our work space.

4. Andrew (build builds) the frame before the twins (cover covers) it with newspaper.

5. The volcano (look looks) somewhat lopsided.

6. Our teacher (point points) out that volcanoes are not a perfect shape.

7. Together we (decide decides) our model is more realistic.

8. A coating of paint (add adds) the finishing touch.

Sailing the Oceans Long Ago

In ancient times, sailors did not have computers and radios to help them find their way. They were guided by landmarks along the coast. They could read the position of the sun and knew what the stars looked like at different times of the year. Also, the newest technology of the time helped guide them across the oceans.

The Compass

The compass is the most basic of the sailor's tools. A compass uses the natural magnetic field of the earth to find directions. By finding north with the compass, the direction of the ship was found by comparing its direction with due north.

The Cross-staff

The cross-staff was used to find latitude early in the 1400s. It was made from two pieces of wood that form a cross. This cross slid up and down a staff. A small hole was drilled at each end of the cross and the end of the staff was fixed. By lining up the holes with a heavenly body and the horizon, the altitude was read on a scale marked on the staff.

The Astrolabe

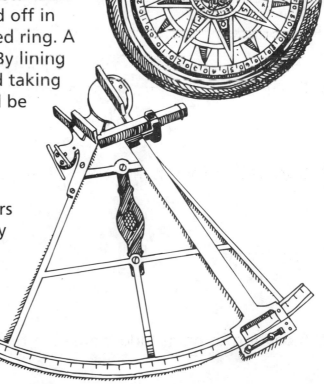

The astrolabe was a wooden or metal disk. The outer edge of the circle was marked off in degrees. It was suspended by an attached ring. A movable pointer pivoted in the center. By lining up the pointer with a distant object and taking readings of the degrees, distances could be found. The astrolabe could be used to determine latitude, longitude, and the time of day.

These instruments guided explorers and sailors for centuries. Over time, they were replaced with more complicated tools made with the latest technology.

Define Vocabulary

These words are found in the passage, "Sailing the Oceans Long Ago". Match each word from the word box to its definition.

ancient	technology	latitude	longitude	horizon
suspend	pivot	instruments	complicated	scale

1. _____ This word describes something that is very old.

2. _____ This is a distance east or west of the prime meridian.

3. _____ This action means to hang freely.

4. _____ These are tools for doing a certain kind of work.

5. _____ This is a distance north or south of the equator.

6. _____ This is an action where something turns on one point.

7. _____ This describes something that is not easy to understand.

8. _____ This noun means the use of science and knowledge to make new things.

9. _____ This is a group of marks used for measuring.

10. _____ This is the line along which the earth and the sky appear to meet.

Nonfiction Reading Comprehension • 3–4 © 2005 Creative Teaching Press

Supporting Details

A paragraph or passage has a main idea. The other sentences provide details that support the main idea. Read each main idea sentence. Cross out the detail sentences that do NOT support the main idea.

1 Main Idea: Sailors look for landmarks to find their way.

    a. A lighthouse on a bluff guides sailors safely into a harbor.
    b. A large boulder on the shore might signal a safe place to anchor.
    c. On a map, a hill might be represented by a small triangle.
    d. The low point between two cliffs might show the mouth of a river.
    e. Sailors kept records during passages for future voyages.

2 Main Idea: Many tools help sailors navigate their ships.

    a. Tools like the sextant help them figure out where they are.
    b. Sailors may remain at sea for months at a time.
    c. The compass helps sailors find where they are going.
    d. The astrolabe was used to find location.
    e. Most sailors can read the position of the sun.

3 Main Idea: Heavenly bodies helped sailors tell time and location.

    a. Mercury is closer to the sun than Venus.
    b. The sun's movement across the sky helped them tell time.
    c. Reading the position of a certain star and the horizon gives the location at sea.
    d. Mechanical clocks were not in wide use until the 14th century.
    e. The position of the constellations changes as location at sea changes.

Use Features of Nonfiction

Nonfiction texts have features that can help you find information. Pictures, captions, chapter titles, subtitles, highlighted vocabulary, and graphic aids are all features that help you use nonfiction texts. For each nonfiction feature write the letter of the matching description and purpose.

1. photographs_____

2. illustrations_____

3. captions_____

4. maps_____

5. tables_____

6. charts_____

7. time lines_____

8. chapter titles_____

9. subtitles_____

10. index_____

11. glossary_____

12. highlighted words_____

a. These headings break down a chapter into smaller sections. Skimming them can help you locate information more quickly.

b. These reproduce an image as it appears in real life and provide examples or details that support the written text.

c. These illustrations show geographic locations in a smaller scale than in real life.

d. This is text that appears below pictures and explains what you are looking at or gives further information about the topic.

e. These can be boldface, italicized, or in color. They signal vocabulary important to the subject you are reading about.

f. These are drawn or painted pictures that show information about the topic.

g. These break a nonfiction book into smaller sections. They give clues about the content of the section.

h. These graphic aids provide information in a brief, organized way. The information is presented in columns and rows.

i. This is an alphabetical listing of topics that appear throughout the book and the page numbers on which you will find each one.

j. These graphic aids shows events in the order that they happened.

k. These graphic aids provide short bits of information in a list. It may include words and numbers.

l. This is an alphabetical listing of all the important vocabulary and their definitions.

Nonfiction Reading Comprehension • 3–4 © 2005 Creative Teaching Press

Identify Homophones

Homophones are words that sound the same but have different meanings and spellings.

Circle the homophone that correctly completes each sentence.

1 The tall masts of the sailing ships were fashioned from (wood would).

2 Our class (read red) a book about great wooden sailing vessels.

3 Trading ships would (by buy) goods in one port to sell in another.

4 Old sailing vessels were (made maid) to travel great distances.

5 A ship could be troubled by stormy weather the entire (way weigh).

6 The captain would (do due) what he had to in order to keep the ship on course.

7 Some passengers were seasick the (hole whole) voyage.

8 Life at (sea see) was difficult and dangerous.

9 As waves tossed the ship, the boards would (creek creak) and groan.

10 A family traveling to the New World would bring only the (bear bare) necessities.

Turtles to Protect

There are many sea turtles in the world's oceans. All of them are threatened. The Kemp's ridley turtle is the most endangered of all. This kind of turtle has almost become extinct many times.

The Kemp's ridley turtle only lays its eggs in one place. A stretch of sandy beach in Mexico is that place. Many female turtles come to shore at the same time. They dig a nest. They lay their eggs. Then they crawl back into the ocean.

The local people watched this amazing sight. Many of these people were poor and hungry. The people started to hunt the turtles. They caught the turtles for meat, and they dug up the eggs to eat. Because hunters took too many turtles, the turtles began to disappear.

In 1947, as many as 40,000 turtles came to shore to lay eggs. In 1989, less than 400 turtles were seen on the beach. Something had to be done. The turtles would soon be extinct.

Today, people are not allowed to hunt turtles. It is against the law to disturb their nests. People protect the turtles when they come onto the beach. They make sure the nests are not bothered. The future for the Kemp's ridley turtles is uncertain. Perhaps people's efforts to protect them will help.

Nonfiction Reading Comprehension • 3–4 © 2005 Creative Teaching Press

Name _____ Date _____

Match Vocabulary

Draw a line to match each word from the passage, "Turtles to Protect" with its meaning.

1 threatened

2 endangered

3 stretch

4 disappear

5 extinct

6 disturb

7 protect

8 uncertain

a. an expanse of space that goes on for a distance

b. to pass out of sight

c. to move out of place

d. to be in danger

e. to keep safe from harm or injury

f. not sure

g. a group of living things that is no longer living

h. a group of living things that is at risk of dying out

Use four vocabulary words from above to complete the sentences.

9 If we do not protect the sea turtles, they are sure to _____.

10 Humans should not disturb the nesting sites on the _____ of beach.

11 Some endangered animals later become _____.

12 The bald eagle is a _____ bird, but its future is no longer uncertain.

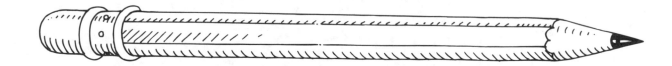

Nonfiction Reading Comprehension • 3–4 © 2005 Creative Teaching Press

Name _____ Date _____

Determine Problem and Solution

A **problem** is something that is difficult or hard to understand. A **solution** is a way to fix, or solve, the problem. Draw a line to match each problem in the left column with a possible solution in the right column.

1 People who are poor and hungry gather the turtles' eggs for food.

2 People leave their trash on the beach.

3 People kill turtles to use their shells to make ornamental items such as combs, clips, and eyeglass frames.

4 Other animals find the nests and eat the eggs.

5 People pour chemicals down storm drains that later wash up on the beach.

6 Boats along the shoreline frighten away the turtles.

a. Provide trashcans along the beach with signs that remind people to keep the beach clean.

b. Paint warnings that remind people that what goes into a storm drain ends up on the beach.

c. Persuade people not to buy tortoise-shell products.

d. Set up a food bank so people can get the food they need.

e. Pass a law that bans boats from the beach area during egg-laying season.

f. Once the turtles have laid their eggs, fence off the nests so predators cannot reach them.

Nonfiction Reading Comprehension • 3–4 © 2005 Creative Teaching Press

Name _____ Date _____

Use a Book Index

An **index** is found in the back of a nonfiction book. An index is an alphabetical listing of topics in the book followed by the page number or numbers where information about the topic can be found. Page numbers in italics refer to pages that have a picture. An entry may also be cross-referenced. In other words, it will tell you what else to look under to find related information. Use the book index to answer the questions.

Index	
Predators	13–19
Sea Turtles	40–49, *51*
Skin	15
Snapping Turtles	13, *20*
Terrapins	19, 26
Tortoises	7, *16*, 19–22
Turtles	7–28
endangered	32, 35, 50–55
food	16, 23, *41*
hibernation	22, 31
nesting	19, *40–42*
prehistoric	9–10
See also **sea turtles, terrapins, tortoises**	
Western Turtles	54

1 On what page would you look to find information on the type of skin turtles have?
    a. page 14
    b. page 13
    c. page 15
    d. page 16

2 On what page would you look to find a picture of a snapping turtle?
    a. page 13
    b. page 17
    c. page 20
    d. page 26

3 On which pages would you read about endangered species of turtles?
    a. 9–14
    b. 13–19
    c. 19–22
    d. 50–55

4 On which page or pages are turtles' nesting habits illustrated?
    a. 16
    b. 19
    c. 9–10
    d. 40–42

5 Were there prehistoric turtles? On which pages would you look to find out?
    a. 4–6
    b. 9–10
    c. 7–28
    d. 13–19

6 When you look under "turtles," what other topics are cross-referenced?
    a. sea turtles
    b. terrapins
    c. tortoises
    d. all of the above

Identify Prefixes

A **prefix** is a word part that is added to a root. A prefix has meaning that it adds to a word.

re- means "again"   *rewind* means "to wind again"
un- means the "opposite of" or "not"   *untie* means the "opposite of tie"
multi- means "many"   *multicolored* means "many colors"
mis- means "bad" or "badly"   *misuse* means "to badly use"

Circle the prefix of each word in the left column. Then write the letter of its matching definition.

1 unusual_____   **a.** badly pronounce

2 misprint_____   **b.** many purposes or uses

3 reboot_____   **c.** not grateful or thankful

4 unknown_____   **d.** not usual

5 mispronounce_____   **e.** badly understand

6 uncertain_____   **f.** a bad print

7 repay_____   **g.** to boot up or start a computer again

8 ungrateful_____   **h.** to pay back or again

9 multipurpose_____   **i.** opposite of "known"

10 misunderstand_____   **j.** not certain

11 rearrange_____   **k.** many types of media

12 multimedia_____   **l.** to arrange again

Nonfiction Reading Comprehension • 3–4 © 2005 Creative Teaching Press

Bartering

Imagine you are a farmer with a small plot of land. On your land you grow corn and wheat. You grow more than enough for your family to eat. Sometimes you think how nice it would be to have some eggs to eat or some fresh milk to drink.

Your neighbor is also a farmer. She does not grow the same things you do. Instead she raises animals. She has cows for milk and chickens for eggs. Your neighbor has plenty to eat, but she does not have room to grow wheat and corn like you do.

But wait! If you have plenty of corn and wheat and she has plenty of milk and eggs, why don't you both trade? The trading of goods like this is called bartering. Before money, humans bartered to get what they needed.

In medieval times, people would gather on market days to barter their goods. Everyone would gather at the lord's castle to offer their goods for sale. A butcher might trade meat for a bag of grain. A weaver might trade a length of cloth for a basket of eggs. With many people gathered together, everyone could barter for the things they could not grow or make themselves.

During times of exploration, people bartered. When Lewis and Clark traveled west, they brought many items to trade with the Native Americans. Lewis and Clark knew they would need to barter for horses, food, and other supplies they could not carry. They brought beads, knives, clothing, and other portable items that the Native Americans might want. They were able to barter with the tribes to get the things they needed.

Then people invented money. Bartering was no longer needed. Money has value on its own. It can be exchanged for all goods. You no longer need to find someone who needs what you have for sale before you can trade.

Nonfiction Reading Comprehension • 3–4 © 2005 Creative Teaching Press

Name _____ Date _____

Complete Sentences with Vocabulary

These words are found in the passage "Bartering". Complete each sentence with a word from the word box.

| neighbor | goods | bartering | medieval | exploration |
| supplies | portable | value | invented | |

1. Someone who lives next door or near to you is called your _____.

2. Many people made trips of _____ to the New World.

3. Things that can be bought or sold are called _____.

4. Explorers needed to bring enough _____ to last the whole trip.

5. Can you picture what life would be like if money had never been

   _____?

6. An object's _____ is what it is worth.

7. _____ is the act of trading one thing for another.

8. If you go backpacking, all of your supplies need to be _____.

9. _____ describes the time of the Middle Ages.

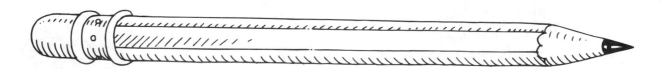

Nonfiction Reading Comprehension • 3–4 © 2005 Creative Teaching Press

Summarize Information

Summarizing means to tell the main ideas of a passage or story. A good summary is brief. It does not include unnecessary details, repeated thoughts, or unimportant ideas. The statements below summarize the first five paragraphs from "Bartering". Circle the letter of the choice that best completes each summary.

Paragraph 1: As a farmer, you grow more than enough of some things, but
- **a.** you will just have to do without other things.
- **b.** you do not grow or raise other things you would like.
- **c.** every year you give everything away.

Paragraph 2: Your neighbor raises things you want, and
- **a.** you will have to talk her into giving you some.
- **b.** she will not give you any unless you give her gold.
- **c.** she would like to have the things you grow.

Paragraph 3: You and your neighbor can
- **a.** trade or barter to get the things you want or need.
- **b.** take what you want when the other is not looking.
- **c.** grow the foods you do not have next year.

Paragraph 4: In medieval times, many people gathered together on market days to
- **a.** persuade the weaver to give them some cloth.
- **b.** barter for things they needed but did not make or raise themselves.
- **c.** buy up all the wheat that a miller had for sale.

Paragraph 5: Bartering was a way for explorers to
- **a.** get the supplies they needed from people they met on their explorations.
- **b.** make new friends with people and get them to do what they wanted.
- **c.** make a lot of money before they headed back home.

Name _____ Date _____

Use a Graphic Source

A **graphic source** is something that shows information visually. Pictures, charts, graphs, and maps are graphic sources. They provide a lot of information that can be seen quickly.

Use the bar graphs below to answer the questions.

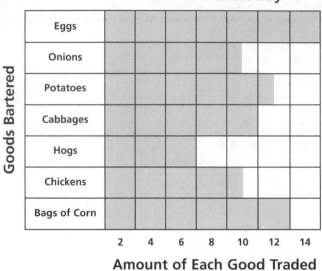

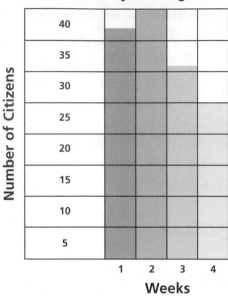

) During which week did the greatest number of citizens attend the market?
a. Week 1   **b.** Week 2   **c.** Week 3   **d.** Week 4

) Which good was bartered for the most?
a. cabbages   **b.** bags of corn   **c.** eggs   **d.** potatoes

) How many bags of corn were traded during market day?
a. 12   **b.** 14   **c.** 10   **d.** 6

) How many more chickens than hogs were bartered?
a. 2 more   **b.** 9 more   **c.** 3 more   **d.** 6 more

) What was the total number of citizens who attended the market in August?
a. 155   **b.** 133   **c.** 126   **d.** 40

) What seems to be the most popular vegetable at the market?
a. eggs   **b.** cabbages   **c.** corn   **d.** onions

Nonfiction Reading Comprehension • 3–4 © 2005 Creative Teaching Press

Name _____ Date _____

Understand Word Suffixes

A **suffix** is a word part that is added to a root. A suffix has meaning that it adds to a word.

-ly means "like" or "in a certain way"
-able means "capable of" or "able to"
-ist means "a person who does, makes, or has to do with a certain thing"
-ment means "the act of" or "process of"

Read the first word in each row. Then circle the meaning that best matches the word.

1	**government**	process of governing	a person who governs
2	**breakable**	able to be broken	a person who breaks things
3	**cowardly**	able to be a coward	like a coward
4	**flutist**	able to play a flute	a person who plays a flute
5	**measurement**	act of measuring	able to measure
6	**lovable**	the process of love	capable of being loved
7	**artist**	a person who makes art	capable of art
8	**quickly**	in a quick manner	a person who is quick
9	**amazement**	act of being amazed	a person who is amazed
10	**machinist**	a machine process	a person who makes machines
11	**friendly**	capable of being a friend	like a friend
12	**washable**	able to be washed	a person who washes

Magnets

A long time ago, people discovered a special type of stone. When they hung these stones from a string, one end of the stone pointed north. These stones were called lodestones, or "leading stones." They could be used to lead people in the direction they wanted to go.

The lodestones are a type of rock called magnetite. Magnetite is naturally magnetic. When a rock is magnetic, it is able to attract other objects that are made from iron or steel.

Magnets are objects that attract or repel iron and steel. There are many types of magnets. All magnets have a north pole and a south pole. The poles are where the force of the magnet is strongest. Opposite ends of a magnet attract each other. The north pole of one magnet attracts the south pole of another. The same ends repel each other. The north pole of one magnet repels the north pole of another.

A magnet can attract objects without touching them. The space around a magnet where its force pulls is called its magnetic field. A magnetic field can attract an object through solids, liquids, and gases.

A compass is a magnet. A compass points north because Earth is a magnet. Earth contains a lot of iron. The north and south poles are where the magnetic pull is the strongest. This is why a compass points north. The north-seeking compass points towards the north pole of Earth.

Nonfiction Reading Comprehension • 3–4 © 2005 Creative Teaching Press

Name _____ Date _____

Search a Vocabulary Puzzle

Use the context of each sentence and find a word from the passage "Magnets" to complete the sentence. Then circle the word in the puzzle below.

1 A _____ is a rock that acts like a magnet.

2 The opposite poles of a magnet _____ each other.

3 Iron is one _____ of metal that is attracted to a magnet.

4 Magnetite is a rock that is _____ magnetic.

5 Each end of a magnet is called a _____.

6 The south poles of two magnets will _____ each other.

7 The space around a magnet where its force pulls is its _____ field.

```
A   D   G   U   H   O   I   R   J   P   K   L   L   R   M
O   N   L   O   D   E   S   T   O   N   E   O   Y   P   P
B   T   V   L   U   Y   T   W   S   O   R   L   Q   A   O
W   Y   A   X   H   Y   A   T   T   R   A   C   T   Z   L
C   P   T   A   W   B   T   K   H   D   G   I   E   E   E
H   E   S   N   A   T   U   R   A   L   L   Y   G   S   F
M   A   G   N   E   T   I   C   H   H   E   D   I   N   J
D   A   Y   K   Y   O   L   E   E   T   R   E   P   E   L
F   S   C   A   N   U   S   M   B   Y   N   A   W   O   P
```

Nonfiction Reading Comprehension • 3–4 © 2005 Creative Teaching Press

Reread and Recall Information

Use what you learned in "Magnets" to choose the best answer. Reread the passage, if necessary, to check your answers.

1 When something is magnetic, it
    a. creates a strong electric shock.
    b. is able to attract iron or steel objects.
    c. is able to affect the weather.
    d. none of the above

2 A type of naturally magnetic rock is
    a. magnetite.
    b. granite.
    c. iron.
    d. all of the above

3 Lodestones were used to
    a. measure weight.
    b. locate sources of water.
    c. guide people in the direction they wanted to go.
    d. none of the above

4 All magnets have
    a. a north and south pole.
    b. a magnetic field.
    c. attracting and repelling ends.
    d. all of the above

5 A magnetic field is
    a. a grassy space around a magnet.
    b. a place outside where natural magnets are found.
    c. the force of pull in the space around a magnet.
    d. none of the above

6 A compass points north because
    a. that is the direction people want to go.
    b. the needle is attracted to Earth's north pole.
    c. it is attracted to the nearest magnet.
    d. all of the above

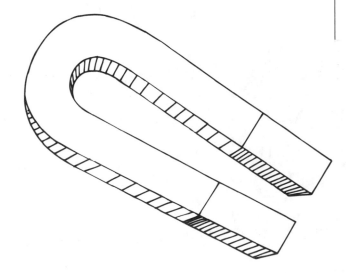
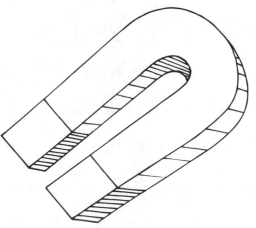

Nonfiction Reading Comprehension • 3–4 © 2005 Creative Teaching Press

Use a Dictionary

A **dictionary** is a book of words and their meanings. All words are listed alphabetically. You can use the guide words at the top of each page to figure out what words are listed on the page. Guide words tell the first and last word on each page.

Use the dictionary guide words to answer the questions.

dig • dimple	200	201	diner • direct

machine • magician	336	337	magnet • maid

1 On which page would you find *magnetism*? _____

2 Would *dirty* come before or after page 201? _____

3 On which page would you find *dilute*? _____

4 Between which two guide words would you find *mackerel*? _____

5 On which page would you find *dime*? _____

6 Between which two guide words would you find *dinner*? _____

Name _____ Date _____

Find Words with Opposite Meanings

Words with opposite meanings are called **antonyms**. Circle the antonym for the underlined word in each sentence.

1 Opposite magnet poles <u>attract</u>.

      catch   repel   defend   attach

2 The force of a magnetic field can be <u>strong</u>.

      tough   weak   small   muscle

3 The surface of the metal is <u>smooth</u>.

      rough   silky   cold   warm

4 Our class was <u>quiet</u> during the test.

      fast   silent   hard   noisy

5 The cookie jar was <u>empty</u>.

      funny   full   last   cold

6 I will <u>close</u> the window for you.

      finish   shut   open   write

7 His big smile showed he was <u>happy</u> to be there.

      sad   funny   laugh   cry

8 The <u>shiny</u> mirror reflected the light.

      smooth   glass   dull   sharp

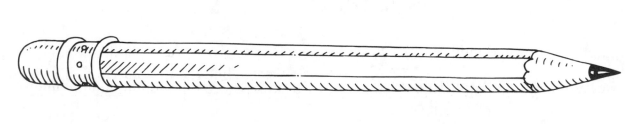

Nonfiction Reading Comprehension • 3–4 © 2005 Creative Teaching Press

Hawks and Owls

A farmer carefully surveys his vineyard. Mice and voles may gnaw on the vines. Small birds may peck at the grapes before they can be picked. The farmer will lose money if he cannot keep the pests away. However, he has a powerful ally in the fight to protect his grape vines. He can count on the help of raptors.

Raptors are also known as birds of prey. All raptors have powerful feet with sharp, curved talons and hooked beaks for tearing flesh. Their strong wings make them powerful fliers. Keen eyesight helps them spot a pest from far away. Two species of raptors that are very helpful to farmers are the red-tailed hawk and the barn owl.

The red-tailed hawk is diurnal, which means it hunts during the day. Hawks can be useful predators of pests. They eat mice, voles, rabbits, and locusts. Hawks hover over the ground below. By floating on air currents in this manner, hawks can get a good view of the landscape below. When a hawk spots its prey, it can swoop down quickly.

Owls are nocturnal, or night hunters. Their large eyes make it possible for them to see well at night. Their eyes are also positioned at the front of their head. This gives owls the ability to judge how far away prey is.

In one year, each hawk or owl can eat as many as 2,000 rodents. After catching and killing an animal, an owl will take it to a nearby branch or perch. The owl proceeds to swallow the animal whole headfirst. Only if the animal is too big to be swallowed whole will the owl tear it into chunks.

Define Vocabulary

These words are found in the passage "Hawks and Owls." Match each word from the word box to its definition.

survey	gnaw	ally	raptor	talons
diurnal	nocturnal	hover	perch	ability

1. _____ This verb means "to chew on something."

2. _____ This is a bird that has talons for catching prey.

3. _____ This describes an animal that is active during the night.

4. _____ This verb means "to look around or examine."

5. _____ This is a branch or rod where a bird can sit.

6. _____ This describes an animal that is active during the day.

7. _____ This verb means "to stay in one place in the air."

8. _____ This is the quality of being able to do something.

9. _____ This noun describes someone or something that has joined forces with another.

10. _____ These are claws of a bird that hunts and catches other animals.

Nonfiction Reading Comprehension • 3–4 © 2005 Creative Teaching Press

Name _____ Date _____

Compare and Contrast Details

When you **compare**, you tell the ways that two or more things are alike. When you **contrast**, you tell the ways that two or more things are different. Use the phrases in the word box to complete the chart comparing and contrasting hawks and owls.

a raptor	has talons	nocturnal	diurnal	keen eyesight
float on air currents	can judge distance	eats rodents	eats small birds	
hooked beaks	helpful to farmers	eyes at front of head		eyes at side of head

Characteristics of Hawks

_____ _____ _____

Both

_____ _____ _____

_____ _____ _____

_____

Characteristics of Owls

_____ _____ _____

Name _____ Date _____

Find Word Meanings

Each entry in a dictionary shows how to spell a word, shows how to pronounce it, names the part of speech, and gives its definitions. Use the information in the dictionary entries to answer the questions.

> **measure** *verb* 1. To find the size, amount, degree, or capacity of: *We measure the box.* 2. To have as a measurement: *The box measures 8 inches wide.* • *noun* 3. A unit used in measuring: *The pint is a liquid measure.* 4. An action taken for a reason: *He took measures to stop the noise.*
>
> **perch**[1] *noun* 1. A branch or rod on which a bird can sit. 2. A place where a person can sit. • *verb* To rest or sit on.
> **perch**[2] *noun* A freshwater food fish of North America and Europe.

1 The entry for *measure* lists how many definitions for its use as a noun?
- **a.** 4
- **b.** 2
- **c.** 3
- **d.** 1

2 The entries for *perch* are followed by a raised number because
- **a.** they are homophones.
- **b.** they are spelled. differently.
- **c.** they are both verbs.
- **d.** they are both fish.

3 Which definition is used in this sentence: *Mom measured my height.*
- **a.** definition 1
- **b.** definition 2
- **c.** definition 3
- **d.** definition 4

4 Which definition is used in this sentence: *The canary perched on my finger.*
- **a.** a freshwater food fish of North America and Europe
- **b.** a branch or rod on which a bird can sit
- **c.** a place where a person can sit
- **d.** to rest or sit on

5 Which definition is used in this sentence: *The new law was a measure against crime.*
- **a.** definition 1
- **b.** definition 2
- **c.** definition 3
- **d.** definition 4

Nonfiction Reading Comprehension • 3–4 © 2005 Creative Teaching Press

Name _____ Date _____

Understand Similes

A **simile** is figurative language that compares two things using the word *like* or *as*. A simile uses the qualities or characteristics of one thing to describe how another thing acts, sounds, looks, or feels.

For each simile in the left column write its intended meaning.

1 My mother has eyes like a hawk. _____

a. He moves in a quick manner.

2 The frightened child was as quiet as a mouse. _____

b. I had to work extra hard to get work done.

3 He moved as quick as a rabbit. _____

c. On a moonless night, it is really dark.

4 It seemed like a heavy black cloak covered the nighttime sky. _____

d. She sees really well.

5 The sunset looked like a painter's masterpiece. _____

e. He moved really slowly.

6 The test was like an uphill battle. _____

f. The test was really hard and took a lot of effort.

7 The boy moved like a snail. _____

g. The child was so scared, she did not make any noise.

8 I felt like a salmon swimming upstream. _____

h. The sunset was very colorful.

Fossils

Fossils are the parts or outlines of a living thing from long ago. Fossils can be made from plants or animals. They might show a skeleton, a shell, or the imprint of a leaf. Fossils are fixed in rock.

We find most fossils in rock made from sediments. Sediment is sand, dirt, and decayed bits of plants and animals. These tiny bits settle to the bottom of a lake or an ocean. The sediments make a layer. The pressure of the water and more layers press the sediments together to make rock. When the rock hardened around the parts of plants and animals, a fossil formed.

There are different kinds of fossils. Sometimes a dead plant or animal rots away. This leaves a hollow space in the rock. The hollow space is the same size and shape as the living thing once was. This is a mold fossil.

If water fills the empty space, the minerals in the water build up. They form the shape of the plant or animal. This is a cast fossil.

Sometimes minerals replace the cells of a dead plant or animal over a long time. The minerals form a rocklike fossil that looks like the live plant or animal. This is a petrified fossil.

A trace fossil is another kind of fossil. It is made when an animal from long ago makes footprints in mud. The mud later turns to rock and the footprints remain.

Fossils help tell the story of life on Earth. They give us clues about plants and animals that lived long ago.

Nonfiction Reading Comprehension • 3–4 © 2005 Creative Teaching Press

Name _____ Date _____

Solve a Vocabulary Puzzle

Use the vocabulary words from the passage "Fossils" to complete the crossword puzzle.

imprint	fixed	decayed	hollow
petrified	trace	remain	clues

Across
3. a mark or pattern made when something is pressed on a surface
5. a visible mark of the former presence of something
7. to go on being
8. when plant or animal matter is completely broken down by bacteria

Down
1. not movable
2. having a space or opening inside
4. when minerals have replaced the cells of dead plants or animals
6. things that help solve a problem or mystery

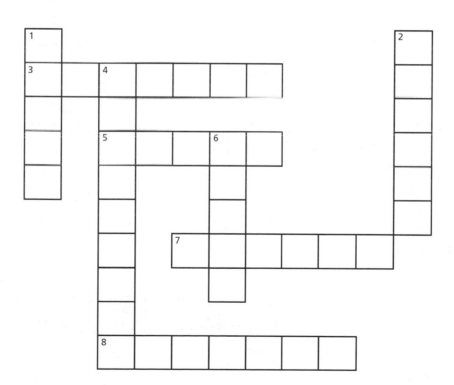

Name _____   Date _____

Determine Order of Events

Key words like *before, after, next, then,* and *following* are words that help you tell the order in which events happen. Use information from "Fossils" to choose the best answer for each question.

1 Fossils can only form
   a. before sediments can settle.
   b. at the same time a living thing exists.
   c. long after a living thing has died.

2 First a plant or animal rots away, and
   a. then there are no more plants or animals.
   b. then a hollow space is left behind.
   c. then it is replaced by a new plant or animal.

3 Before a fossil can form,
   a. sediments must settle over objects to make a layer.
   b. water must disappear.
   c. earthquakes and volcanoes destroy the objects.

4 After a hollow space is formed,
   a. it collapses from the pressure.
   b. it fills with air from the atmosphere.
   c. it next fills with minerals to make a cast fossil.

5 Following a long period of time, a petrified fossil can be made
   a. before a plant or animal has died.
   b. after the cells are replaced by minerals.
   c. after sediments bury a footprint.

6 Before a trace fossil can appear,
   a. an animal first leaves a footprint in the mud.
   b. a plant has to sink into the mud.
   c. scientists must uncover it with tools.

Nonfiction Reading Comprehension • 3–4 © 2005 Creative Teaching Press

Name _____ Date _____

Read a Tree Diagram

A **tree diagram** is a picture that maps out how things are related. A family tree is one such diagram. The tree diagram below shows the different kinds of plants that have been found as fossils. Use the diagram and the words in the word box to complete the statements.

conifers	angiosperm	bryophytes	monocot	liverworts	tree

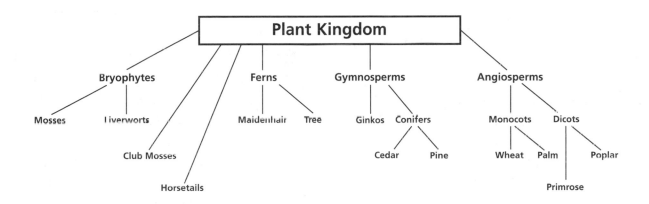

1 The mosses are most closely related to the _____.

2 If a plant is a(n) _____, it can be either a monocot or a dicot.

3 Cedars and pines are examples of _____.

4 Liverworts are a smaller group within the _____.

5 A palm tree is an example of a _____.

6 Two examples of ferns are the maidenhair and the _____.

Understand Compound Words

Compound words are formed from two other words. The meanings of both words contribute to the meaning of the compound word. Complete each sentence by combining a word in the left box with a word in the right box to make a compound word.

mail	pop	with		out	shore	stairs
night	sea	base		corn	box	ball
down	out			gown	side	

◗ The letter was waiting for me in the _____.

◗ Our next vacation will be down by the _____.

◗ Sherry put on her new _____ and went to bed.

◗ Can you even make cookies _____ any eggs?

◗ Tony left his backpack _____, but he cannot remember where.

◗ Mom took us to play _____ at the park.

◗ All of our bedrooms are _____ in our house.

◗ Let's make some _____ and watch a movie.

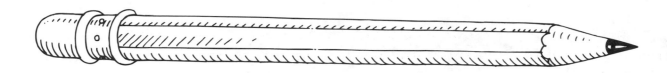

Nonfiction Reading Comprehension • 3–4 © 2005 Creative Teaching Press

Eleanor of Aquitaine

The year 1122 was a long time ago. It was a time long before the United States existed. It was the time when castles were built. Kings and queens ruled the land. It was the year Eleanor of Aquitaine was born.

Eleanor was the daughter of a rich man. Her father owned the lands of Aquitaine. When her father died in 1137, she inherited all of the lands. Eleanor was already beautiful. Now she was rich. She would also prove to be wise.

That same year, Eleanor married the King of France. At first, the king was happy. He took over Eleanor's lands when they married. Eleanor was not happy. The people of France did not like her. She did not like this new place. After fifteen years, the marriage was annulled.

That same year, Eleanor married the King of England. He was happy because now he owned Aquitaine. In 1154, her husband was crowned King Henry II. Eleanor was happy because she helped her husband rule. Eleanor and Henry had eight children. Life was good for a while. Then Henry grew tired of Eleanor. She moved into a castle of her own.

Queen Eleanor invited artists and musicians to her court. She asked the best poets and writers of Europe to come to her kingdom. She encouraged both men and women to be creative. She taught manners to her knights, making them the first "gentlemen."

In 1173, Queen Eleanor found out her sons wanted to revolt against their father, the king. She told them this was a good idea. When the king found out, he locked Eleanor in a castle. Few people could visit her. There she remained until Henry died sixteen years later. After her release, Eleanor helped her sons rule the kingdom. She died in 1204.

Name _____ Date _____

Define Vocabulary

These words are found in the passage "Eleanor of Aquitaine". Match each word from the word box to its definition.

existed	inherited	prove	wise
musician	court	encouraged	revolt

1) _____ This means that something was alive at one time.

2) _____ This means having or showing intelligence or good judgment.

3) _____ This is the place where a ruler lives.

4) _____ This verb means "to have received money or property after someone's death."

5) _____ This verb means "to have inspired someone to do something."

6) _____ The verb means "to take part in a rebellion against a ruler."

7) _____ This verb means "to show something to be true."

8) _____ This is a person who is skilled in music, especially as a composer or performer.

Nonfiction Reading Comprehension • 3–4 © 2005 Creative Teaching Press

Name _____   Date _____

Recall and Infer Information

Use what you learned in "Eleanor of Aquitaine" to choose the best answer.

1 How did Eleanor prove she was wise?
- **a.** She helped her husband rule a kingdom.
- **b.** She made her court a place people wanted to be.
- **c.** both a and b

2 How did Eleanor make the knights into the first "gentlemen"?
- **a.** She taught them manners.
- **b.** She encouraged them to wear silk and velvet.
- **c.** She taught them how to fight.

3 How did Eleanor become a rich young woman?
- **a.** Her husband died and left her his wealth.
- **b.** Her father died and she inherited his property.
- **c.** She was wise in business and earned the money.

4 Why did Henry II lock Eleanor in a castle?
- **a.** He had grown tired of her and wanted her out of the way.
- **b.** She had sided with her sons in a revolt against him.
- **c.** both a and b

5 Queen Eleanor lived to be how old?
- **a.** 86 years old
- **b.** 72 years old
- **c.** 82 years old

6 What kinds of people did Eleanor's court attract?
- **a.** creative people like artists, musicians, and poets
- **b.** adventurous people like knights and explorers
- **c.** wise people like scholars, monks, and writers

Create a Time Line

Use the events in the word box to label the dates on the time line of Eleanor of Aquitaine's life.

Eleanor dies   Marries Henry of England
First marriage annulled   Eleanor is born
Marries King of France   Eleanor is imprisoned
King Henry II dies   Eleanor is released
Inherits father's properties   Henry becomes King Henry II of England

1122 _____

1137 _____

_____

1152 _____

_____

1154 _____

1173 _____

1189 _____

_____

1204 _____

Nonfiction Reading Comprehension • 3–4 © 2005 Creative Teaching Press

Name _____ Date _____

Multiple-Meaning Words

Many words have more than one meaning. To decide which meaning of a word is correct, look for clues in the surrounding sentence or paragraph. Read each sentence. Then circle the letter of the correct meaning.

1 The teacher asked me to flip the switch before she started the video.
In this sentence, *switch* means
   a. to change.
   b. a thing that turns electricity on and off.

2 Mrs. Murphy asked Quinn and Ryan to switch desks.
In this sentence, *switch* means
   a. to change.
   b. a thing that turns electricity on and off.

3 The machinery's loud racket made us cover our ears.
In this sentence, *racket* means
   a. a great deal of noise.
   b. equipment used to play tennis.

4 Thwack! The racket squarely struck the ball.
In this sentence, *racket* means
   a. a great deal of noise.
   b. equipment used to play tennis.

5 I cannot go outside to play until I fully recover from the flu.
In this sentence, *recover* means
   a. bring back to normal condition.
   b. get well.

6 The police were able to recover the stolen car.
In this sentence, *recover* means
   a. locate.
   b. get well.

Cycle of Nature

The sun rises over the mountains. Its light reflects off the surface of a pond. A light breeze softly blows. The reeds in the water sway in the breeze. Gnats buzz by. A water skipper floats on the pond's surface. The croak of a frog breaks the silence. Suddenly, a trout leaps high into the air. These things are all part of the cycle of nature.

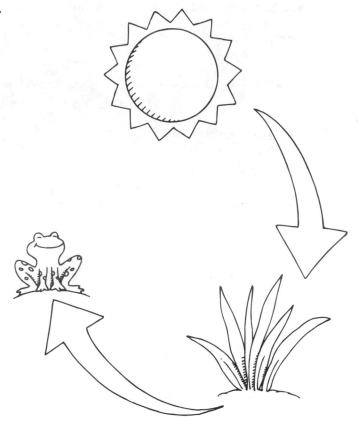

A habitat is made up of living and nonliving things. The sunlight, water, rocks, and dirt are nonliving. The frog, reeds, insects, and trout are living. Together they are the habitat of a pond.

All living things need energy to live. All living things need food for energy. Living things depend on nonliving things to get energy. Living things also depend on each other.

A living thing is a producer, a consumer, or a decomposer. Producers make their own food. Plants are producers. They use sunlight, water, and nutrients to make food. Consumers cannot make their own food. They eat other living things to get their energy. Animals and humans are consumers. When plants and animals die, they become food for decomposers. These are living things that break something down into smaller pieces. Worms and germs are decomposers.

Together living things make a cycle. The producers use nutrients to make food. The consumers eat the producers and each other. The decomposers break down their remains. The nutrients become part of the ecosystem. Then the cycle starts over.

Nonfiction Reading Comprehension • 3–4 © 2005 Creative Teaching Press

Name _____ Date _____

Solve a Vocabulary Puzzle

Use the vocabulary words from the passage "Cycle of Nature" to complete the crossword puzzle.

breeze	reeds	sway	croak	habitat
depend	nutrient	ecosystem	cycle	

Across
1. a low, hoarse sound such as that made by a frog or crow
2. to fall back on for support
4. the plants, animals, and nonliving things that make up an environment
6. a light wind
7. the place where a plant or an animal naturally lives and grows
8. to swing back and forth from side to side

Down
1. a series of events that are regularly repeated in the same order
3. something that nourishes a living thing
5. tall grasses with hollow stems that grow in wet places

Name _____ Date _____

Reread and Recall Information

Use what you learned in "Cycle of Nature" to choose the best answer. Reread the passage, if necessary, to check your answers.

1 A habitat is
   a. light off the surface of a pond.
   b. needed for energy for living things.
   c. made up of living and nonliving things.

2 Examples of nonliving parts of a habitat are
   a. sunlight, water, rocks, and dirt.
   b. water, soil, seaweed, and sunlight.
   c. dirt, rocks, sand, and insects.

3 Examples of living parts of a habitat are
   a. insects, birds, plants, and soil.
   b. mammals, birds, rocks, and snails.
   c. plants, reptiles, frogs, and birds.

4 Producers are
   a. animals that produce eggs.
   b. plants that make their own food.
   c. plants that are dead and decaying.

5 Consumers are
   a. animals that get energy from other living things.
   b. plants that use water and sunlight for food.
   c. animals that eat only plants.

6 What is cycled from the habitat to producers to consumers to decomposers and back into the habitat?
   a. reeds
   b. sunlight
   c. nutrients

Nonfiction Reading Comprehension • 3–4 © 2005 Creative Teaching Press

Order a Circular Story

A **circular story** is one in which the events or steps in the story come around so that the ending is also the beginning. Cycles in nature and the life cycles of living things make good subjects for circular stories. Use these parts of the water cycle to complete the diagram for a circular story. Use the illustrations as clues.

The sun heats the water.
The water evaporates.
The water vapor rises into the air.
Streams of water form a lake.

The water runs down to form a stream.
Raindrops bounce off or sink into the earth.
The water vapor condenses and forms clouds.
Precipitation leaves the clouds.

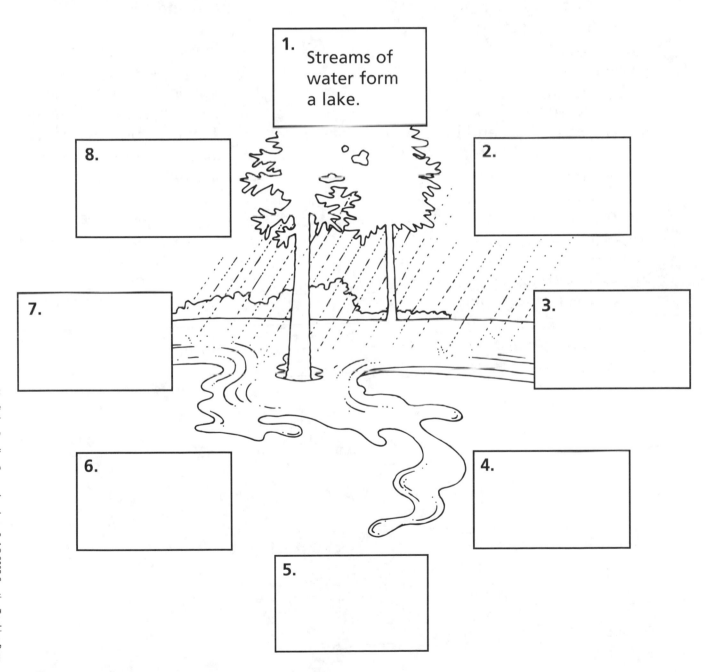

1. Streams of water form a lake.

8.

2.

7.

3.

6.

4.

5.

Name _____ Date _____

Define Idioms

Idioms are expressions. Their meaning cannot be understood from the meanings of each word in the sentence. Instead, idioms have a different meaning altogether. Choose the best meaning for these common idioms.

1 Wow! It is raining <u>cats and dogs</u> outside!
   a. cats and dogs fell from the sky
   b. raining really hard and fast
   c. flooding streets

2 When my mom saw the mess she <u>hit the roof</u>.
   a. acted really excited
   b. jumped up and bonked her head on the ceiling
   c. got really mad

3 Our neighbor <u>let the cat out of the bag</u>.
   a. released a cat from a bag
   b. could not keep a secret
   c. keeps many pets

4 Last week's math test was a <u>piece of cake</u>.
   a. cake was exchanged for math papers
   b. really easy
   c. tasty and sweet

5 I would believe him because <u>a leopard cannot change his spots</u>.
   a. someone's belief or behavior does not change
   b. a leopard tried to dye its hair and could not
   c. someone who lies

6 Hurry up! The <u>coast is clear</u>.
   a. danger is near
   b. no clouds at the beach
   c. safe to go on

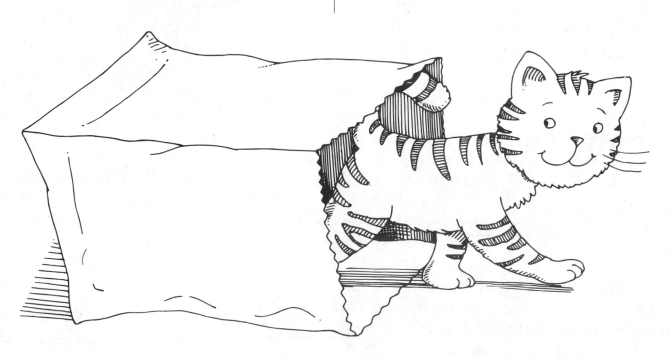

Nonfiction Reading Comprehension • 3–4 © 2005 Creative Teaching Press

Chief Joseph

Chief Joseph was born around 1840 in the Wallowa Valley of Oregon. His Nez Perce name was Hin-mah-too-yah-lat-kekt, which meant "thunder coming up the water over the land." Chief Joseph led his people at a time when they had many problems with the United States government.

The Nez Perce people had always believed in peace with the whites who were moving to their lands. As more people came, the land seemed smaller and smaller. Soon, the government told the Nez Perce they had to move to a reservation in Idaho. It was one-tenth the size of the land they had been promised.

Joseph became chief when his father died in 1871. The problems were getting worse. Chief Joseph believed in peaceful resistance. He did not believe in violence. The government promised many things. Chief Joseph refused to take his people to the reservation. Then an army general threatened to attack if his people did not go. Chief Joseph made the only decision he could. He would lead his people toward Idaho, even though he did not want to.

The group never got there. A few Nez Perce warriors were angry about losing their land. They made a raid on nearby settlers and killed several people. The army went after Chief Joseph's band. Chief Joseph had no choice but to side with the other war leaders who wanted to fight.

For about three months, a band of 700 Native American men, women, and children fought bravely against 2,000 U.S. soldiers. In the end, they could not win. They surrendered in 1877. Chief Joseph said, "…I am tired. My heart is sick and sad. From where the sun now stands I will fight no more forever."

For the rest of his life, Chief Joseph spoke out about the poor treatment of his people by the United States government.

Nonfiction Reading Comprehension • 3–4 © 2005 Creative Teaching Press

Define Vocabulary

These words are found in the passage "Chief Joseph." Match each word from the word box to its definition.

surrender raid	reservation settlers	resistance government	violence decision

1 _____ This is the ability to resist or to keep from giving in.

2 _____ This is the result of making up one's mind.

3 _____ This is land set apart by the government for a certain purpose.

4 _____ This is a sudden attack.

5 _____ This is the use of physical force to cause damage or injury.

6 _____ This is a group of people who keep a country under control.

7 _____ This means to give up to another in response to a demand or to force.

8 _____ These are people who move to live in a new area.

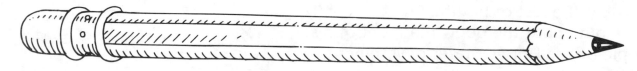

Nonfiction Reading Comprehension • 3–4 © 2005 Creative Teaching Press

Paraphrase Meaning

Paraphrasing is explaining something in your own words. After you read a passage, you can restate the main idea in a new way. You should not add your own opinion or change the author's meaning. Paraphrasing can help you remember new ideas.

Read each set of sentences. Then circle the statement that best paraphrases the original idea.

1 The Nez Perce people tried to solve problems peacefully. They honored treaties. They kept their promises. They were willing to share their land with the settlers.

    a. The Nez Perce tried many ways to keep the peace with newcomers.
    b. People often solve problems by working together.
    c. Promises are meant to be broken.

2 Chief Joseph said, "...I am tired. My heart is sick and sad. From where the sun now stands I will fight no more forever."

    a. Chief Joseph became ill because he had been standing too long in the hot sun.
    b. Chief Joseph surrendered because he was upset about all the fighting.
    c. If you fight too much, you will become sad and tired.

3 The U.S. government made treaties with the Nez Perce. They promised them large areas of land. They promised payment for what the tribe would give up. The land turned out to be very small. The payments never came.

    a. The treaties the U.S. government offered the Nez Perce were fair.
    b. The U.S. government ran out of money before it could pay the Nez Perce.
    c. Treaties for land and money for the Nez Perce were often not kept.

4 In spring and summer, some Native American groups dressed in their colorful costumes. Other times, drums could be heard throughout the region. The voices of the singers mix with the autumn air. Many feasts marked the arrival of edible plants and the run of salmon.

    a. Native American groups enjoyed singing and dancing.
    b. Native Americans enjoyed edible plants and salmon.
    c. Native American groups gathered for celebrations throughout the year.

Name _____ Date _____

Read a Historical Map

A **historical map** shows what places were like long ago. They also show where important events took place or the routes people traveled. This map shows the Trail of Tears, routes used by the U.S government to take Native Americans to the newly established reservations.

Use the historical map to answer the questions.

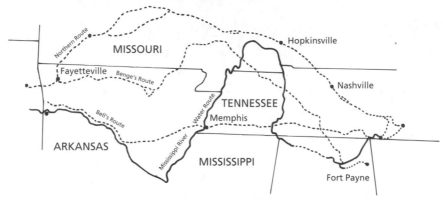

1 Which route followed the course of the Mississippi River?
   a. Northern Route
   b. Bell's Route
   c. Water Route

2 Which route began at Fort Payne and ended at Fayetteville?
   a. Northern Route
   b. Bell's Route
   c. Benge's Route

3 Which route passes by Nashville and Hopkinsville?
   a. Northern Route
   b. Bell's Route
   c. Benge's Route

4 Which route never passed through Missouri?
   a. Northern Route
   b. Bell's Route
   c. Water Route

5 How many routes passed through Memphis, Tennessee?
   a. one
   b. two
   c. three

Nonfiction Reading Comprehension • 3–4 © 2005 Creative Teaching Press

Name _____ Date _____

Identify Base Words

Many words are formed by adding a prefix to the beginning or a suffix to the end of a word. The word you start with is the base word. Use a word from the word box to complete each sentence. Then find the base word in each word you chose. Write the base word on the second line.

unharmed	peaceful	disagree	misbehaved
undo	graceful	disappeared	treatment

1 Chief Joseph protested the _____ of his people.

_____

2 The old way of life has now _____.

_____

3 It is fine to _____, but we should not fight over it.

_____

4 Once we have done hurtful things, we cannot _____ them.

_____

5 Chief Joseph's wish was that his people would remain _____.

_____

6 Chief Joseph tried to resist the government in a _____ way.

_____

7 No one _____ on the field trip, so our guides complimented us.

_____

8 The dancers' _____ movements captured our attention.

_____

Forty-Niners

In January of 1848, James Marshall was supervising the building of a sawmill. As he walked along a ditch that carried water to the mill, he saw something shiny. Little golden pebbles, about the size of peas, lay at the bottom of the ditch. He picked one up. It looked like gold. He pounded it. It bent but did not break. It was gold!

In December of 1848, the president told Congress about the discovery in California. In 1849, people rushed to California. They wanted to look for gold. They became known as forty-niners.

The forty-niners were mostly men, but there were some women, too. Immigrants from around the world joined the race for gold. More than 50,000 people traveled to California hoping to get rich. They had to deal with many hardships. Illness, harsh living conditions, awful weather, and crime did not stop them. The dream of gold kept the forty-niners going.

Forty-niners moved from one mining camp to another. Each time they hoped to strike it rich. They did find gold, but it never lasted long. Some gambled it away. Others spent what they found to pay high prices for supplies.

Many people needed food and lodging. There was not enough of either to go around. Prices went up. A small room that normally rented for $5 now cost $50. A new pair of boots might cost $100. A shovel sold for $50. The forty-niners spent money as fast as they earned it. The shopkeepers got rich.

The forty-niners spent more money than they made. Some returned to their homes far away. Others settled down in the new state. Whatever they chose to do, the forty-niners remain a part of our nation's history.

Nonfiction Reading Comprehension • 3–4 © 2005 Creative Teaching Press

Name _____ Date _____

Match Vocabulary

Draw a line to match each word from the passage "Forty-Niners" with its meaning.

1 supervising

2 ditch

3 pebble

4 sawmill

5 immigrants

6 hardship

7 gambled

8 lodging

a. a place where lumber is cut

b. something that causes suffering or difficulty

c. a long, narrow trench

d. watching over and inspecting work as it is done

e. people who come to live in a new country

f. a place to stay for a short time

g. a small, round stone

h. took a chance

Use four vocabulary words from above to complete the sentences.

9 Mr. Marshall was supervising the building of a _____ when gold was discovered.

10 Many _____ gambled that they would strike it rich.

11 A lack of lodging was but one _____ the miners faced.

12 That single golden _____ found at the sawmill changed the history of California forever.

Name _____ Date _____

Make Generalizations

A **generalization** is a statement about what several people or things have in common. Words like *sometimes, many, much, all, most,* and *never* can signal a generalization.

Circle **yes** or **no** to tell if each statement is a generalization.

1 Most miners spent more money on supplies than they earned.   yes   no

2 Levi Strauss sold canvas jeans during the Gold Rush.   yes   no

3 Miners sometimes gambled away their earnings.   yes   no

4 All miners faced many hardships when traveling to California.   yes   no

5 Gold is a valuable mineral.   yes   no

A **valid generalization** is supported by facts and logic. A **faulty generalization** is not. Circle the answer that best describes each of the following statements.

6 With the discovery of gold, everyone rushed to California.
   a. a faulty generalization because not every person went there
   b. a valid generalization because the discovery was announced to Congress
   c. a faulty generalization because everyone went to Nevada

7 Most people spent a fortune for food and lodging.
   a. a valid generalization because prices were high and newcomers needed these things
   b. a faulty generalization because very few people needed a place to stay
   c. a valid generalization because miners are rich and will pay any price

8 After the Gold Rush, none of the miners returned to their previous homes.
   a. a valid generalization because everyone had come to California from the east
   b. a valid generalization because no one would want to stay when they were poor
   c. a faulty generalization because some miners returned to their previous homes

Nonfiction Reading Comprehension • 3–4 © 2005 Creative Teaching Press

Read a Schedule

A **schedule** is a special chart that lists events and tells when they will take place. The schedule below shows when certain activities and events will take place during a gold rush celebration day. Use the schedule to answer the questions.

Gold Rush Days Celebration
Thursday, July 8 through Sunday, July 11
Old County Park
9:30 a.m. to 5:00 p.m. daily
All activities are daily.

Activity	Times				
Panning for Gold	10:00	11:15	12:30	3:00	4:30
Discovery Reenactment		11:40	1:40		
Tug-of-War Competition	10:30		1:00	3:45	
Three-legged Race	10:00	11:30	12: 45	3:00	4:45
Hand-mucking*	10:15	11:15	12:15	2:15	3:15

*shoveling tailings by hand

1 Which activity can you do earliest on any of the days?
 a. three-legged race or hand-mucking
 b. panning for gold or tug-of war competition
 c. panning for gold or three-legged race

2 Which is the last activity held before the park closes?
 a. panning for gold
 b. three-legged race
 c. tug-of-war competition

3 At 11:15, which activities can you do?
 a. panning for gold or three-legged race
 b. panning for gold or hand-mucking
 c. hand-mucking or tug-of-war competition

4 Which event could you do at only three different times each day?
 a. tug-of-war competition
 b. discovery reenactment
 c. panning for gold

5 How many times during the entire celebration will the reenactment be held?
 a. two times
 b. four times
 c. eight times

Name _____ Date _____

Write Irregular Plural Nouns

Most nouns are made plural by adding *–s* or *–es*. Irregular plural nouns are not formed this way. Instead, irregular plurals have different spellings than their singular forms. There are even irregular plurals that do not change at all. You only know they are plural from how they are used in the sentence.

Write the irregular plural forms of these nouns. Use a dictionary if you are unsure of the spelling.

1 goose	_____		**6** mouse	_____
2 man	_____		**7** tooth	_____
3 woman	_____		**8** ox	_____
4 foot	_____		**9** child	_____
5 deer	_____		**10** moose	_____

Use the irregular plurals from above to complete the sentences.

11 The herd of _____ shook their antlers and stomped their

_____.

12 Two _____ leaped over the fence, flicked their tails, and bounded off.

13 "We would like many _____ that lay golden eggs," cried the group

of 5-year-old _____.

14 Not many _____ traveled to the gold fields, but there were

plenty of _____.

15 Remember to brush your _____ before you go to bed.

16 I can hear the scurry of _____ behind our kitchen wall.

Marco Polo

Marco Polo was born in Venice, Italy in 1254. At this time, people did not know much about faraway places. Travel was hard. It was often dangerous.

Marco's father was an explorer. He had already traveled to faraway places. When Marco was seventeen, his father and uncle decided to bring Marco with them.

The dynasty of China was far away from Venice. It was a great civilization ruled by the emperor Kublai Khan. Other explorers brought back stories about wonderful cities. The Polos decided they would travel there. It took them four years to reach China.

When the Polos arrived in China, they were not disappointed. They saw the emperor's palace built from shining marble and gold. They saw exotic animals and birds. The emperor himself dressed in long robes of silk covered in jewels. They saw many new products like silk cloth, tea, spices, and noodles. They knew people back in Europe would want these new things.

Marco quickly learned the language of this new land. This impressed the emperor. He made Marco a member of his government. The emperor sent Marco on important missions around his empire. Marco stayed in China for many years.

Marco Polo returned home to find his city at war. He was taken prisoner. While in prison, he told his story to another prisoner. He told about the things he had seen in China. The prisoner wrote Polo's stories down. His stories became popular all over Europe. Some of them seem unbelievable. Today we are not sure how much of his tale is true.

When Marco Polo was on his deathbed, he was asked to tell if his tales were false. He replied that he had only told half of what he had seen.

Nonfiction Reading Comprehension • 3–4 © 2005 Creative Teaching Press

Name _____ Date _____

Define Vocabulary

These words are found in the passage "Marco Polo." Match each word from the word box to its definition.

| tales | explorer | exotic | impressed | disappointed |
| mission | dangerous | dynasty | civilization | |

1 _____ This describes something or someone from a different part of the world.

2 _____ This is a person who travels through an unknown or unfamiliar place.

3 _____ This means to have failed to satisfy the wishes of someone.

4 _____ This describes something full of risk or harm.

5 _____ This is a group of people who show a high level of accomplishment in language, science, agriculture, and art.

6 _____ This is a succession of rulers from the same family.

7 _____ This means to have had a strong favorable effect on someone.

8 _____ This is an assignment or task to be carried out.

9 _____ These are stories that are quite often made up.

Nonfiction Reading Comprehension • 3–4 © 2005 Creative Teaching Press

Use Prior and Learned Knowledge

Sometimes you can predict why something happened because of what you have learned or what you already know. Use the information in "Marco Polo" and your own judgment to choose the most likely answer to each question.

1 Most likely, people did not know much about faraway places because
   a. they were lazy and did not want to leave home.
   b. travel to these places was difficult and dangerous.
   c. transportation had not yet been invented.

2 The emperor most likely sent Marco Polo on missions because
   a. he did not have anyone else to send.
   b. he was impressed by Polo's abilities and accomplishments.
   c. Polo was annoying and people wanted him out of the way.

3 The Polos were probably not disappointed when they reached China because
   a. there were so many exotic things like gold, silk, and strange animals.
   b. they already knew what they would find when they got there.
   c. the emperor would be very unhappy if they were disappointed.

4 Most likely, the Polos knew people in Europe would like the new exotic things because
   a. they could read people's minds.
   b. they had asked for a wish list from people before they left Europe.
   c. people like to buy what is new and different.

5 If Marco Polo had not been imprisoned, quite possibly
   a. his stories would never have been written down.
   b. he would have died in China.
   c. he would have brought silk to the New World.

6 Marco Polo's tales were probably popular because
   a. the book had really interesting illustrations.
   b. people liked to hear about strange and exotic places.
   c. people felt like they had to read the stories.

Name _____ Date _____

Determine Author's Purpose

The **author's purpose** is the reason an author has for writing. Usually, the author does not tell you directly why he or she is writing a passage. The four most common purposes for writing nonfiction are to persuade, to inform, to entertain, and to express.

Circle the author's purpose for each passage.

1 Marco Polo may have been young, but was he experienced! He traveled across thousands of miles, serving as his own pack animal. He learned a new language faster than you can say, "Kublai Khan."

      entertain   persuade   inform   express

2 The history and culture of China go back thousands of years. The Chinese system of writing is over 4,000 years old. They also perfected porcelain, papermaking, lacquer finishes, and detailed jade and ivory carvings.

      entertain   persuade   inform   express

3 I feel that Marco Polo probably never went to China. He did not tell of things that would have been part of Chinese life. He does not mention tea drinking. He does not talk about calligraphy. Most unusual of all, he never mentions the Great Wall of China.

      entertain   persuade   inform   express

4 I love reading about Marco Polo. His adventures, even though over 700 years old, convince me that I should experience the vibrant setting of the sun through another culture's eyes. I am truly inspired by the adventures of this man.

      entertain   persuade   inform   express

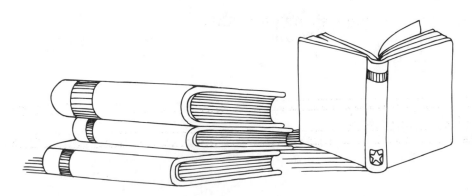

Nonfiction Reading Comprehension • 3–4 © 2005 Creative Teaching Press

Use Verb Tenses: Present, Past, Future

Verbs in the present tense tell what is happening now:
travels   *stops*   *carry*   *explore*   *goes*

Verbs in the past tense show actions that have already happened.
traveled   *stopped*   *carried*   *explored*   *went*

Verbs in the future tense show an action that will happen and include the helping verb *will*.
will travel   *will stop*   *will carry*   *will explore*   *will go*

Underline the verb in each sentence. Write **past, present,** or **future** to tell the tense of the verb.

1 Marco Polo traveled to the Orient.   _____

2 We will study for our test on Friday.   _____

3 My grandmother watches old movies.   _____

4 Tori shops for new sneakers.   _____

6 The Wilsons took a long vacation.   _____

5 My brother and I will need new school supplies.   _____

7 Al and Amy walk quickly.   _____

8 The chorus sang for the visitors yesterday.   _____

Mission San Carlos Borromeo de Carmelo

Junipero Serra was a Franciscan monk. When he was a young man, he was asked to go to Alta California. He would start several missions there. Each mission would have a church to teach the native people the Christian religion. Each mission would grow food and raise cattle. The missions would help Spain watch over this new land.

Mission San Carlos Borromeo de Carmelo was the second mission built by Father Serra. This mission was supposed to be at the shore of Monterey Bay. The padres decided that the soil was not good for growing crops. The mission would have to be moved somewhere else. Not far away, the padres found the beautiful Carmel Valley. This place was perfect. Father Serra wanted to make this mission the head of all the missions to follow.

In 1771, Father Serra moved into the new Carmel Mission. The first church and houses were made of wood. They were enclosed by a palisade of poles. The early years were hard. The padres depended on the Indians for supplies. Soon the mission was able to grow what it needed. Adobe structures replaced the wooden buildings.

Father Serra always considered this mission to be his home. When he died in 1784, Serra asked that he be buried there. Altogether, twenty-one missions were built along the California coast. Father Serra started eight of them in his lifetime. His favorite was always the Carmel Mission.

Solve a Vocabulary Puzzle

Use the vocabulary words from the passage "Mission San Carlos Borromeo" to complete the crossword puzzle.

monk	mission	cattle	soil
palisade	padre	adobe	consider

Across
1. a man who belongs to a religious group
2. to think about before deciding
3. the loose top layer of the earth's surface

Down
1. a place at which missionaries live or work
2. large, heavy animals raised for meat, hides, or milk
4. a fence of high, pointed sticks to protect against attack
5. Spanish for "father," the name given to a member of the clergy
6. brick made of clay and straw that has dried in the sun

Nonfiction Reading Comprehension • 3-4 © 2005 Creative Teaching Press

Determine Fact and Opinion

A **fact** is something that can be proved true or false. Statements of facts can be proved by checking reference books, measuring, experimenting, and observing. An **opinion** tells a person's ideas or feelings. It cannot be proved true or false. It can be explained. Opinions often have "good" words such as *beautiful, best, great,* and *better* or "bad" words such as *ugly, cruel, awful,* and *worst*.

Write **opinion** or **fact** to identify each statement.

1. _____ The journey to the mission was difficult.

2. _____ Junipero Serra was a Franciscan monk.

3. _____ Father Serra built the best missions.

4. _____ There were twenty-one missions built along the California coast.

5. _____ People at the mission traded with the Indians.

6. _____ Adobe houses are very beautiful and cozy.

7. _____ One mission was built in Carmel Valley.

8. _____ Father Serra started eight missions in his lifetime.

9. _____ The Carmel Mission was the greatest mission ever built.

10. _____ Each mission grew food and raised its own cattle.

Nonfiction Reading Comprehension • 3–4 © 2005 Creative Teaching Press

Read a Historical Map

A **historical map** can show the sites of places that are important to history. Use the map of the California missions to choose the best answer.

Write the sentence choice that forms the main idea for each paragraph.

1 Which mission was founded first?
- **a.** San Gabriel
- **b.** San Carlos
- **c.** San Diego
- **d.** San Antonio de Padua

2 Which mission was the last to be founded?
- **a.** Santa Inés
- **b.** San Rafael
- **c.** San Francisco Solano
- **d.** San Fernando

3 Which mission is closest to Mexico?
- **a.** San Luis Rey
- **b.** San Juan Capistrano
- **c.** San Diego
- **d.** Soledad

4 Which mission was not founded in 1797?
- **a.** San Luis Rey
- **b.** San Fernando
- **c.** San Miguel
- **d.** La Purísima Concepcion

5 How many missions were founded from 1797 to 1817?
- **a.** 7
- **b.** 9
- **c.** 5
- **d.** 21

San Francisco Solano (1823)
San-Rafael (1817)
San Francisco (1776)
San José (1797)
Santa Clara (1777)
Santa Cruz (1791)
San Juan Bautista (1797)
San Carlos (1770)
Soledad (1791)
San Antonio de Padua (1771)
San Miguel (1797)
San Luis Obispo (1772)
Santa Inés (1804)
La Purísima Concepcion (1787)
Santa Barbara (1786)
San Buenaventura (1782)
San Fernando (1797)
San Gabriel (1771)
San Juan Capistrano (1776)
San Luis Rey (1797)
San Diego (1769)

Identify More Synonyms

Remember that a **synonym** is a word that means the same or almost the same as another word. Write each word from the word box next to its synonym in the list below.

speak	pail	father	enjoy	shut	yelled	difficult
middle	stone	soil	smart	near	leave	ill
wash	simple	seat	silly	create	story	

1 like _____

2 center _____

3 rock _____

4 bucket _____

5 dirt _____

6 close _____

7 go _____

8 hard _____

9 sick _____

10 easy _____

11 close _____

12 talk _____

13 clever _____

14 clean _____

15 shouted _____

16 chair _____

17 funny _____

18 dad _____

19 make _____

20 tale _____

Nonfiction Reading Comprehension • 3–4 © 2005 Creative Teaching Press

Earth's Continents

Look at a map of Earth and you will see a lot of blue. That blue shows all the oceans of the world. The oceans separate the continents from each other. A continent is one of the main land masses on Earth. There are seven continents.

The smallest continent is Australia. It is the only continent that is also a country and an island. Europe is the second smallest continent. Its borders are made by seas, rivers, and the Atlantic Ocean. Europe has many islands and peninsulas.

The largest continent is Asia. Asia has one-third of all the land on Earth. It also has the largest population. Africa is the second largest continent. It has the world's largest desert and longest river. Both Africa and Asia have been home to some of the world's oldest cultures.

North America is the third largest continent. South America is fourth largest. Together, these two continents make up what was called the New World. Both are surrounded by the Pacific Ocean to the west and the Atlantic Ocean to the east.

Antarctica is bigger than Europe but smaller than South America. It covers the South Pole. Antarctica is covered with ice all year round.

Together the continents make up the world we live in.

Name _____ Date _____

Solve a Vocabulary Puzzle

Use the vocabulary words from the passage "Earth's Continents" to complete the crossword puzzle.

separate	border	mass	island
peninsula	seas	population	culture

Across

1. a piece of land that sticks out into water from a larger land mass
3. to divide into parts
5. bodies of water within an ocean and partly enclosed by land
7. a piece of land, smaller than a continent, completely surrounded by water

Down

1. the total number of people living in a certain place
2. the customs, beliefs, ways of living, and craftwork that belong to a people
4. the line or outside edge that marks the end of something
6. something large in size

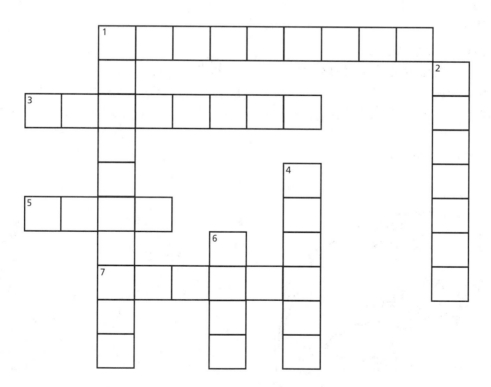

Nonfiction Reading Comprehension • 3–4 © 2005 Creative Teaching Press

Name _____ Date _____

Reread and Recall Information

Use what you learned in "Earth's Continents" to choose the best answer. Reread the passage, if necessary, to check your answers.

1 The continents are separated by Earth's
   a. seas.
   b. oceans.
   c. rivers.

2 The continent that is also an island is
   a. New Zealand.
   b. Hawaii.
   c. Australia.

3 Asia is largest because
   a. it has the world's largest population.
   b. it has the world's largest land mass.
   c. both a and b

4 Africa is a continent that has
   a. the world's biggest population and forest.
   b. the world's biggest desert and longest river.
   c. the world's longest river and highway.

5 The New World was made up of
   a. North and South America.
   b. Asia and Africa.
   c. Australia and Asia.

6 Antarctica
   a. is covered by ice.
   b. covers the South Pole.
   c. both a and b

Nonfiction Reading Comprehension • 3–4 © 2005 Creative Teaching Press

Name _____ Date _____

Use a Table

This table has facts about the five oceans of the earth. Use the table to answer the questions.

Ocean Name	Size (sq. miles)	Deepest Point (feet)	Location
Atlantic	33,420,000	Puerto Rico Trench, 28,231	between North America and Europe; between South America and Africa
Arctic	5,106,000	Eurasia Basin, 17,881	surrounds the North Pole
Indian	28,350,000	Java Trench, 25,344	between Africa and Australia; below Asia
Pacific	64,186,000	Mariana Trench, 36,200	between Asia and North America; between Australia and South America
Southern	7,848,300	South Sandwich Trench, 23,736	surrounds Antarctica

1 Which ocean is the deepest? _____

2 Which ocean is the smallest? _____

3 Which ocean is the largest? _____

4 What is the name of the deepest point in the Indian Ocean?

_____

5 If you wanted to touch the Southern Ocean, to which continent would you travel?

_____

6 Which ocean has a deepest point of 28,231 feet? _____

Nonfiction Reading Comprehension • 3–4 © 2005 Creative Teaching Press

Identify More Antonyms

Remember that an antonym is a word that means the opposite of another word. Write each word from the word box next to its antonym in the list.

gloomy	nice	feast	famished	polite	sell	awake
worst	found	patient	shallow	sick	hello	cowardly
never	pull	straight	above	receive	whisper	

1 mean _____

2 best _____

3 doctor _____

4 impudent _____

5 always _____

6 push _____

7 happy _____

8 buy _____

9 bent _____

10 healthy _____

11 snack _____

12 lost _____

13 deep _____

14 goodbye _____

15 full _____

16 brave _____

17 below _____

18 give _____

19 shout _____

20 asleep _____

The Lincoln Memorial

Look at the back of a penny. There you will see one of our country's best-known buildings, the Lincoln Memorial. This structure honors one of our greatest presidents, Abraham Lincoln. It is well known that the memory includes a statue of Lincoln. Did you know that the memorial has many other symbols to honor the president, our country, and the hard time we faced long ago?

Construction began on the memorial in 1914. The building was designed to look like a Greek temple. It was built out of granite, marble, and limestone. The details of the memorial have special meanings.

The outside of the building has 36 columns. Each column stands for one of the 36 states that made up the United States when Lincoln died. The name of a state is carved on each column. Above these are the names of the 48 states that existed when the memorial was built.

The inside of the building has three rooms. The middle room has the statue of Abraham Lincoln seated in a chair. He faces the Capitol building and the Washington Monument. In the south room, the Gettysburg Address, a famous speech, are carved on a stone tablet. A mural shows an angel freeing a slave. In the north room, the speech Lincoln gave when he was elected president a second term is carved on a stone tablet. A mural there shows the union of the North and the South. This memorial reminds us of what Lincoln did for our country.

The memorial became a part of our history in 1922. It was dedicated on February 12, Abraham Lincoln's birthday. Lincoln's son, Robert Todd Lincoln, was the guest of honor at the ceremony.

Nonfiction Reading Comprehension • 3–4 © 2005 Creative Teaching Press

Name _____ Date _____

Complete Sentences with Vocabulary

These words are found in the passage "The Lincoln Memorial." Complete each sentence with a word from the word box.

honor	construction	memorial	tablet
mural	dedicated	union	ceremony

1 The people of the United States wanted to _____ President Lincoln.

2 The _____ is in Washington, D.C., not far from the one honoring the Vietnam veterans.

3 The _____ of the memorial took many years.

4 A painted _____ tells the story of how Lincoln kept our country together.

5 The finished memorial was _____ on Lincoln's birthday.

6 Lincoln's Gettysburg Address is inscribed on one stone _____.

7 A mural shows the _____, or joining, of the North and South after the Civil War.

8 When the memorial was completed, a _____ was held to open it to the public.

Nonfiction Reading Comprehension • 3–4 © 2005 Creative Teaching Press

Recall Main Idea and Details

Use the information in "The Lincoln Memorial" to choose the best answer.

1. What is the main idea of the fourth paragraph?
   a. The three rooms of the memorial have special features.
   b. The three rooms of the memorial took a long time to build.
   c. Two of the three rooms have murals.

2. Which of the following is not a detail of the second paragraph?
   a. It was built of marble, granite, and limestone.
   b. It was built to look like a Greek temple.
   c. It has many columns.

3. Which best describes the main idea of the third paragraph?
   a. The building could not stand without columns.
   b. The columns were made of a special type of stone.
   c. The columns represent the United States.

4. Which of the following is not a detail of the fifth paragraph?
   a. The memorial was dedicated on Lincoln's birthday.
   b. Lincoln's son was the guest of honor.
   c. Many famous people attended the ceremony.

5. What is the main idea of the fifth paragraph?
   a. The Lincoln Memorial is an outstanding monument.
   b. The Lincoln Memorial became a part of U.S. history in 1922.
   c. Abraham Lincoln was a much-loved president.

6. What is the best-known part of the Lincoln Memorial?
   a. the statue of Lincoln's Gettysburg address
   b. the statue of a standing Lincoln
   c. the statue of a seated Lincoln

Nonfiction Reading Comprehension • 3–4 © 2005 Creative Teaching Press

Name _____ Date _____

Check for True or False Statements

These statements are based on the information in "The Lincoln Memorial." Some are false; some are true. Remember to be true, the entire statement must be true. Write **true** or **false** to identify each statement. Reread the passage to check your answers.

1 The Lincoln Memorial was completed in 1914. _____

2 Each column stands for a former U.S. president. _____

3 The seated figure of Lincoln faces the Capitol building. _____

4 The Gettysburg Address is the only thing carved on a stone tablet.

_____

5 Lincoln was elected for a second term. _____

6 One of the murals shows an angel freeing a slave. _____

7 The memorial was dedicated on February 12, the birthday of Lincoln's son.

_____

8 The Lincoln Memorial appears on the back of the nickel. _____

9 Forty-eight states existed when the memorial was built. _____

10 The inside of the memorial is divided into three rooms. _____

Choose Homonyms

Remember that homonyms are words that sound the same but are spelled differently and have different meanings. Complete each sentence by circling the correct homonym.

1. Mr. Phelps lost all of his hair and now he is _____.

bald
bawled

2. We had to _____ water out of our rowboat.

bale
bail

3. My _____ arms got sunburned today.

bare
bear

4. There is an important _____ in the contract.

claws
clause

5. The dog began to _____ when the fire siren went off.

wail
whale

6. The boat almost capsized on the high _____.

seas
seize

7. It took over an _____ for the car to be fixed.

hour
our

8. We could not find _____ house on the long street.

there
their

Nonfiction Reading Comprehension • 3–4 © 2005 Creative Teaching Press

The Voyages of Henry Hudson

Henry Hudson was a sailor born in England, probably sometime in the 1560s. At this time, many goods were arriving from the Orient. The trip over land to the Orient was long and difficult. People wanted to find a different route. Perhaps a Northwest Passage could be found by sailing across the ocean.

Searching for the Northwest Passage

In 1607, Hudson set sail across the Atlantic Ocean with his son and eleven crew to look for a Northwest Passage. They sailed closer to the North Pole than any previous ship. There was no way through the North Pole. They had to return to England.

The Second Voyage

In 1608, Hudson set sail again. This time he took a different route. He saw his first Arctic summer because at the northern tip of Norway the sun shines 24 hours a day. He still did not find a Northwest Passage.

Sailing for Holland

In 1609, Hudson moved to Holland and sailed for a Dutch company. That same year, he sailed north from Amsterdam to look for the passage. Right away the weather turned bad and the crew began to grumble about mutiny. Hudson turned south. They ended up off the coast of Maine. He explored Cape Cod and the Chesapeake Bay. After traveling north, the ship dropped anchor in a great river we know today as the Hudson. He claimed this entire region for Holland.

The Last Voyage

In 1610, Hudson set forth on his fourth voyage. The weather was foul and icy for the entire trip. Then Hudson sighted an enormous body of water he thought was the Pacific Ocean. At last Hudson thought he had found the Northwest Passage, but it turned out to be a bay. Now the ship was out of food and the men were angry. The crew mutinied and put Hudson to sea. No one knows what became of Hudson. Today many landmarks bear his name.

Name _____ Date _____

Match Vocabulary

Draw a line to match each word from the passage "The Voyages of Henry Hudson" with its meaning.

1. Orient
2. route
3. crew
4. previous
5. grumble
6. mutiny
7. anchor
8. foul

a. to complain or mutter

b. a line of travel between two places

c. existing or taking place earlier

d. name for the countries of Asia

e. stormy and unpleasant

f. open rebellion by sailors against their captain

g. people who work together to operate a ship

h. a heavy metal device dropped into the water to keep a ship in one place

Use four vocabulary words from above to complete the sentences.

9. Many people wanted to find a new _____ to the Orient.

10. The previous day, the crew dropped the _____ in the bay.

11. When the weather turned foul, the crew thought about _____.

12. The crew began to _____ about the bad conditions.

Nonfiction Reading Comprehension • 3–4 © 2005 Creative Teaching Press

Name _____ Date _____

Tell Fact from Opinion

Remember that a **fact** is a statement that can be proven or disproven. An **opinion** is how someone feels or believes. An opinion cannot be proven, but it can be explained. In each pair of statements, circle the one that is a fact.

1 a. Henry Hudson went off in search of a Northwest Passage.
   b. Henry Hudson was a poor navigator.

2 a. The crew was hostile and no longer happy.
   b. The crew declared mutiny against their captain.

3 a. Hudson was put to sea with his son and a few other sailors.
   b. Hudson was upset he had been treated so badly.

4 a. Hudson captained for a company in Holland.
   b. It was a good company to work for.

5 a. Henry treated his sailors poorly.
   b. Three times a day the sailors received their rations.

6 a. The sailing vessel was made on the coast of England.
   b. It was an excellently built sailing ship.

7 a. A sailor would climb the mast and watch for land.
   b. The sailor was very brave to climb so high.

8 a. The waves and weather were the roughest the men had ever seen.
   b. The waves measured thirty feet at times.

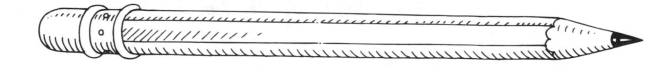

Name _____ Date _____

Read a Historical Map

This map shows each of the four voyages of Henry Hudson. Use the map to answer the questions.

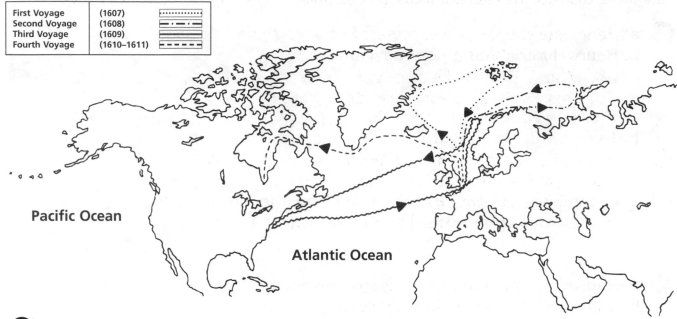

First Voyage (1607) ·············
Second Voyage (1608) — · — · —
Third Voyage (1609) ——————
Fourth Voyage (1610–1611) — — — —

Pacific Ocean

Atlantic Ocean

1 How can you tell that Hudson did not return after his fourth voyage?
   a. The line does not loop back to Europe.
   b. The line goes to Africa.
   c. The line loops back to another country.

2 From what continent did Hudson leave when beginning his voyages?
   a. North America
   b. Greenland
   c. Europe

3 What body of water did Hudson cross to look for the Northwest Passage?
   a. Indian Ocean
   b. Pacific Ocean
   c. Atlantic Ocean

4 On which voyage does it appear Hudson traveled the most distance?
   a. First Voyage
   b. Second Voyage
   c. Third Voyage

Nonfiction Reading Comprehension • 3–4 © 2005 Creative Teaching Press

Choose Homographs

A **homograph** is a word that has different meanings. The same spelling is used for each meaning. You must read the sentence around the word to find out which meaning is used. Read the sentence. Choose the sentence below that uses the underlined word in the same way.

1 We took a <u>trip</u> to the Grand Canyon.
    a. Be careful not to trip on the carpet.
    b. Mom had to make a special trip to the store.
    c. I have seen six people trip on that tree root.

2 Jose gripped the <u>bat</u> tightly as he waited for the pitch.
    a. A bat flew around my head at dusk.
    b. The kittens bat around a ball of yarn.
    c. He swung the bat and hit a home run.

3 Please turn on the <u>light</u> because it is too dark to read.
    a. A full moon will light up the sky.
    b. As the sun went down, the street light came on.
    c. This pillow is light and fluffy.

4 The crowd watched the cars <u>race</u> around the track.
    a. My grandfather owns an antique race car.
    b. I will race you to the fence and back.
    c. The five-mile race will be held this weekend.

5 The rope looked like it would <u>snap</u> if he climbed it.
    a. A snap tore off of my jacket.
    b. That dog is mean, and he will snap at you.
    c. The rubber band will snap if you stretch it too far.

6 The child tried to <u>roll</u> the ball across the playground.
    a. I buttered a roll for my dinner.
    b. Mom needs a new roll of waxed paper.
    c. Please help me roll up this mat.

Answer Key

Define Vocabulary (page 6)

1. cushions
2. rigid
3. cranium
4. direction
5. joints
6. skeleton
7. organs
8. femur
9. vertebrae
10. cartilage

Recall Information (page 7)

1. b
2. b
3. a
4. d
5. a
6. c
7. d
8. d

Identify Main Idea and Details (page 8)

1. a
2. c
3. c
4. b

Identify Nouns, Verbs, and Adjectives (page 9)

1. c
2. a
3. b
4. b
5. c
6. b
7. a
8. c
9. a
10. a

Solve a Vocabulary Puzzle (page 11)

Across

2. gas
4. pitch
6. direction
7. wave
8. intensity

Down

1. vibration
3. solid
5. liquid

Determine Cause and Effect (page 12)

1. Cause: Bell was loud.
   Effect: Everyone jumped in their seats.
2. Cause: Blades were spinning.
   Effect: A whirring sound was heard.
3. Cause: Vibrations reach the ear.
   Effect: We hear a sound.
4. Cause: I was underwater.
   Effect: Pipe clanging was louder.
5. Cause: Sound waves move fast.
   Effect: We hear a high-pitched sound.
6. Cause: Sound travels far.
   Effect: The sound is weak.

Choose Key Words (page 13)

1. c
2. b
3. c
4. a
5. b
6. c
7. c
8. c

Compare with Adjectives (page 14)

1. softer, softest
2. louder, loudest
3. weaker, weakest
4. faster, fastest
5. slower, slowest

The following should be circled:
6. better, best
7. worse, worst

8. faster
9. best
10. weaker
11. softest
12. loudest

Match Vocabulary (page 16)

1. d
2. a
3. g
4. c
5. h
6. e
7. b
8. f
9. thorax
10. abdomen
11. chemical
12. communicate
13. jointed
14. indented
15. boundaries
16. antennae

Summarize Ideas (page 17)

1. Bees use flower nectar to make honey to use as food.
2. The praying mantis eats insects that are pests to gardeners and farmers.
3. Termites are both troublesome and helpful because they eat wood.

Read a Diagram (page 18)

1. abdomen
2. antennae
3. compound eye
4. wings
5. head
6. pollen basket
7. mandibles
8. proboscis
9. stinger

Know Word Roots (page 19)

1. geo; study of the earth, rocks
2. pend; an object that hangs
3. chron; a record of events over time
4. geo; a person who studies the earth
5. chron; to make something happen at the same time
6. micro; a very small living thing
7. scrib; to write words into something
8. pend; a part of the body that hangs down from another part
9. port; to carry out
10. port; able to be carried

Define Vocabulary (page 21)

1. sculpt
2. massive
3. scrape
4. erode
5. formation
6. particle
7. glacier
8. canyon
9. statue
10. surface

Determine Sequence (page 22)

A. 2, 5, 3, 1, 4
B. 5, 3, 2, 4, 1
C. 3, 2, 1, 5, 4

Read a Map Diagram (page 23)

1. desert
2. gulf
3. island
4. hill
5. mountain
6. lake
7. plain
8. valley
9. lake, gulf
10. plain, desert, island, peninsula, valley
11. An island is completely surrounded by water.
12. A mountain is much larger.

Choose Synonyms (page 24)

The following words should be circled:
1. large, huge, bulky
2. scuff, remove, scratch
3. carve, whittle
4. hasty, rapid, swift
5. breeze, gale
6. unhurried, idle
7. stone, boulder, pebble
8. view, watch
9. planet, world
10. brook, creek

Solve a Vocabulary Puzzle (page 26)

Across
1. purpose
3. geography
4. symbol
5. feature
6. detail
7. nation

Down
1. physical
2. continent

Draw Conclusions (page 27)

1. c
2. d
3. b
4. b
5. a
6. b
7. d

Use Map Features (page 28)

1. c
2. a
3. d
4. d
5. c
6. b

Identify Proper Nouns (page 29)

1. America the Beautiful
2. Hawaii
3. Cathedral Peak
4. Indian Ocean
5. Kalahari Desert
6. George Washington
7. Sheryl Crow
8. British Columbia
9. Canada
10. Lord of the Rings
11. North Dakota
12. Nile

Match Vocabulary (page 31)

1. c
2. h
3. e
4. a
5. g
6. d
7. f
8. b
9. orbit
10. rusty
11. reflect
12. swirl

Reread and Recall Facts (page 32)

1. nine
2. heavenly
3. inner planets
4. closest
5. clouds
6. sunlight
7. ice
8. clouds
9. red
10. rusty
11. iron
12. valleys
13. dry
14. polar
15. caps

Read a Table (page 33)

1. Mercury, Venus, Earth, Mars, Pluto
2. Saturn
3. Jupiter
4. they both have one
5. Pluto; It is farthest from the sun.
6. They get colder.

Use Subject and Verb Agreement (page 34)

1. circle
2. cover
3. heats
4. measures
5. studies
6. orbit
7. appear
8. looks
9. learn
10. spies

Solve a Vocabulary Puzzle (page 36)

Across

2. law
4. forced
6. crowded
8. rule
9. colonists

Down

1. crossed
3. agreement
5. religion
7. worship

Infer Sequence (page 37)

6, 2, 3, 1, 5, 9, 7, 10, 4, 8
Paragraphs will vary.

Read a Chart (page 38)

1. false
2. false
3. true
4. false
5. true
6. true

Identify Words as Nouns or Verbs (page 39)

1. noun
2. verb
3. noun
4. noun
5. noun
6. verb
7. verb
8. noun
9. verb
10. verb

Complete Sentences with Vocabulary (page 41)

1. magma
2. fracture
3. plates
4. movements
5. lava
6. buckle
7. dome
8. pressure
9. volcano
10. layers

Find Cause and Effect (page 42)

1. a
2. c
3. b
4. c
5. a
6. c

Use Parts of a Book (page 43)

1. c
2. b
3. b
4. a
5. c
6. b

Choose Present Tense Verbs (page 44)

1. makes
2. gathers
3. spread
4. builds, cover
5. looks
6. points
7. decide
8. adds

Define Vocabulary (page 46)

1. ancient
2. longitude
3. suspend
4. instruments
5. latitude
6. pivot
7. complicated
8. technology
9. scale
10. horizon

Supporting Details (page 47)

The following should be crossed out:
1. c, e
2. b, e
3. a, d

Use Features of Nonfiction (page 48)

1. B
2. F
3. D
4. C
5. H
6. K
7. J
8. G
9. A
10. I
11. L
12. E

Identify Homophones (page 49)

1. wood
2. read
3. buy
4. made
5. way
6. do
7. whole
8. sea
9. creak
10. bare

Match Vocabulary (page 51)

1. d
2. h
3. a
4. b
5. g
6. c
7. e
8. f
9. disappear
10. stretch
11. extinct
12. threatened

Determine Problem and Solution (page 52)

1. D
2. A
3. C
4. F
5. B
6. E

Use a Book Index (page 53)

1. c
2. c
3. d
4. d
5. b
6. d

Identify Prefixes (page 54)

1. d
2. f
3. g
4. i
5. a
6. j
7. h
8. c
9. b
10. e
11. l
12. k

Complete Sentences with Vocabulary (page 56)

1. neighbor
2. exploration
3. goods
4. supplies
5. invented
6. value
7. bartering
8. portable
9. medieval

Summarize Information (page 57)

The following should be circled:
1. b
2. c
3. a
4. b
5. a

Use a Graphic Source (page 58)

1. b
2. c
3. a
4. c
5. b
6. c

Understand Word Suffixes (page 59)

1. process of governing
2. able to be broken
3. like a coward
4. a person who plays a flute
5. act of measuring
6. capable of being loved
7. a person who makes art
8. in a quick manner
9. act of being amazed
10. a person who makes machines
11. like a friend
12. able to be washed

Search a Vocabulary Puzzle (page 61)

1. lodestone
2. attract
3. type
4. naturally
5. pole
6. repel
7. magnetic

```
A   D   G   U   H   O   I   R   J   P   K   L   L   R   M
O   N   L   O   D   E   S   T   O   N   E   O   Y   P   P
B   T   V   L   U   Y   T   W   S   O   R   L   Q   A   O
W   Y   A   X   H   Y   A   T   T   R   A   C   T   Z   L
C   P   T   A   W   B   T   K   H   D   G   I   E   E   E
H   E   S   N   A   T   U   R   A   L   L   Y   G   S   F
M   A   G   N   E   T   I   C   H   H   E   D   I   N   J
D   A   Y   K   Y   O   L   E   E   T   R   E   P   E   L
F   S   C   A   N   U   S   M   B   Y   N   A   W   O   P
```

Reread and Recall Information (page 62)

1. b
2. a
3. c
4. d
5. c
6. b

Use a Dictionary (page 63)

1. page 337
2. after
3. page 200
4. machine and magician
5. page 200
6. diner and direct

Find Words with Opposite Meanings (page 64)

1. repel
2. weak
3. rough
4. noisy
5. full
6. open
7. sad
8. dull

Define Vocabulary (page 66)

1. gnaw
2. raptor
3. nocturnal
4. survey
5. perch
6. diurnal
7. hover
8. ability
9. ally
10. talon

Compare and Contrast Details (page 67)

Characteristics of Hawks

diurnal   float on air currents   eyes at side of head

Both

a raptor
keen eyesight
eat rodents
hooked beaks
has talons
helpful to farmers
eats small birds

Characteristics of Owls

nocturnal   can judge distance
eyes at front of head

Find Word Meanings (page 68)

1. b
2. a
3. a
4. d
5. d

Understand Similes (page 69)

1. d
2. g
3. a
4. c
5. h
6. f
7. e
8. b

Solve a Vocabulary Puzzle (page 71)

Across

3. imprint
5. trace
7. remain
8. decayed

Down

1. fixed
2. hollow
4. petrified
6. clues

Determine Order of Events (page 72)

1. c
2. b
3. a
4. c
5. b
6. a

Read a Tree Diagram (page 73)

1. liverworts
2. angiosperm
3. conifers
4. bryophytes
5. monocot
6. tree

Understand Compound Words (page 74)

1. mailbox
2. seashore
3. nightgown
4. without
5. outside
6. baseball
7. downstairs
8. popcorn

Define Vocabulary (page 76)

1. existed
2. wise
3. court
4. inherited
5. encouraged
6. revolt
7. prove
8. musician

Recall and Infer Information (page 77)

1. c
2. a
3. b
4. b
5. c
6. a

Create a Timeline (page 78)

1122—Eleanor is born
1137—Inherits father's properties/Marries King of France
1152—First marriage annulled/Marries Henry of England
1154—Henry becomes King Henry II of England
1173—Eleanor is imprisoned
1189—King Henry II dies/Eleanor is released
1204—Eleanor dies

Multiple-Meaning Words (page 79)

1. b
2. a
3. a
4. b
5. b
6. a

Solve a Vocabulary Puzzle (page 81)

Across
1. croak
2. depend
4. ecosystem
6. breeze
7. habitat
8. sway

Down
1. cycle
3. nutrient
5. reeds

Reread and Recall Information (page 82)

1. c
2. a
3. c
4. b
5. a
6. c

Order a Circular Story (page 83)

1. streams of water form a lake
2. the sun heats the water
3. the water evaporates
4. the water vapor rises into the air
5. the water vapor condenses and forms clouds
6. precipitation leaves the clouds
7. raindrops bounce off or sink into the earth
8. the water runs down to form a stream

Define Idioms (page 84)

1. b
2. c
3. b
4. b
5. a
6. c

Define Vocabulary (page 86)

1. resistance
2. decision
3. reservation
4. raid
5. violence
6. government
7. surrender
8. settlers

Paraphrase Meaning (page 87)

The following should be circled:
1. a
2. b
3. c
4. c

Read a History Map (page 88)

1. c
2. c
3. a
4. b
5. b

Identify Base Words (page 89)

1. treatment; treat
2. disappeared; appear
3. disagree; agree
4. undo; do
5. unharmed; harm
6. peaceful; peace
7. misbehaved; behave
8. graceful; grace

Match Vocabulary (page 91)

1. d
2. c
3. g
4. a
5. e
6. b
7. h
8. f
9. sawmill
10. immigrants
11. hardship
12. pebble

Make Generalizations (page 92)

1. yes
2. no
3. yes
4. yes
5. no
6. a
7. a
8. c

Read a Schedule (page 93)

1. c
2. b
3. b
4. a
5. c

Write Irregular Plural Nouns (page 94)

1. geese
2. men
3. women
4. feet
5. deer
6. mice
7. teeth
8. oxen
9. children
10. moose
11. moose, feet
12. deer
13. geese, children
14. women, men
15. teeth
16. mice

Define Vocabulary (page 96)

1. exotic
2. explorer
3. disappointed
4. dangerous
5. civilization
6. dynasty
7. impressed
8. mission
9. tales

Use Prior and Learned Knowledge (page 97)

1. b
2. b
3. a
4. c
5. a
6. b

Determine Author's Purpose (page 98)

1. entertain
2. inform
3. persuade
4. express

Use Verb Tenses: Present, Past, Future (page 99)

The following should be underlined:
1. traveled — past
2. will study — future
3. watches — present
4. shops — present
5. took — past
6. will need — future
7. walk — present
8. sang — past

Solve a Vocabulary Puzzle (page 101)

Across

1. monk
2. consider
3. soil

Down

1. mission
2. cattle
4. palisade
5. padre
6. adobe

Determine Fact and Opinion (page 102)

1. opinion
2. fact
3. opinion
4. fact
5. fact
6. opinion
7. fact
8. fact
9. opinion
10. fact

Read a Historical Map (page 103)

1. c
2. c
3. c
4. d
5. a

Identify More Synonyms (page 104)

1. enjoy
2. middle
3. stone
4. pail
5. soil
6. near or shut
7. leave
8. difficult
9. ill
10. simple
11. shut or near
12. speak
13. smart
14. wash
15. yelled
16. seat
17. silly
18. father
19. create
20. story

Solve a Vocabulary Puzzle (page 106)

Across

1. peninsula
3. separate
5. seas
7. island

Down

1. population
2. culture
4. border
6. mass

Reread and Recall Information (page 107)

1. b
2. c
3. c
4. b
5. a
6. c

Use a Table (page 108)

1. Pacific
2. Arctic
3. Pacific
4. Java Trench
5. Antarctica
6. Atlantic

Identify More Antonyms (page 109)

1. nice
2. worst
3. patient
4. polite
5. never
6. pull
7. gloomy
8. sell
9. straight
10. sick
11. feast
12. found
13. shallow
14. hello
15. famished
16. cowardly
17. above
18. receive
19. whisper
20. awake

Complete Sentences with Vocabulary (page 111)

1. honor
2. memorial
3. construction
4. mural
5. dedicated
6. tablet
7. union
8. ceremony

Recall Main Idea and Details (page 112)

1. a
2. c
3. c
4. c
5. b
6. c

Check for True or False Statements (page 113)

1. false
2. false
3. true
4. false
5. true
6. true
7. false
8. false
9. true
10. true

Choose Homonyms (page 114)

The following should be circled:
1. bald
2. bail
3. bare
4. clause
5. wail
6. seas
7. hour
8. their

Match Vocabulary (page 116)

1. d
2. b
3. g
4. c
5. a
6. f
7. h
8. e
9. route
10. anchor
11. mutiny
12. grumble

Tell Fact from Opinion (page 117)

The following should be circled:
1. a
2. b
3. a
4. a
5. b
6. a
7. a
8. b

Read a Historical Map (page 118)

1. a
2. c
3. c
4. c

Choose Homographs (page 119)

1. b
2. c
3. b
4. b
5. c
6. c